OVERNIGHT Date D

D1281302

THE NEW
BRAHMINS
Scientific Life in America

THE NEW BRAHMINS

Scientific Life
in America · by
Spencer Klaw

1968  NEW YORK

WILLIAM MORROW & COMPANY · INC ·

Copyright © 1968 by Spencer Klaw

All rights reserved. No part of this book may be
reproduced or utilized in any form or by any means,
electronic or mechanical, including photocopying,
recording or by any information storage and re-
trieval system, without permission in writing from
the Publisher. Inquiries should be addressed to
William Morrow and Company, Inc., 425 Park
Avenue South, New York, N.Y. 10016.

Published simultaneously in Canada by
George J. McLeod Limited, Toronto.

Printed in the United States of America.

JOINT UNIVERSITY
LIBRARIES
NASHVILLE, TENN.

TITLE II

Q
147
.K55
Science

607786

For Bobby

ACKNOWLEDGMENTS

I am deeply grateful to the scientists who gave me so generously of their time, and who were so patient with an interviewer who was not always sure what questions he should ask. I owe an additional debt of gratitude to the sociologists, psychologists, and other varieties of social scientists from whose writings about American scientists I have extracted so many facts, ideas, and examples. I have, of course, acknowledged this debt in the usual manner, by citing my sources. But I would like to single out for mention here five books that seem to me, considering the way I have plundered their contents, to deserve something more than a footnote. They are: *The Academic Marketplace* by Theodore Caplow and Reece J. McGee; *Graduate Education in the United States* by Bernard Berelson; *The Effects of Federal Programs on Higher Education* by Harold Orlans; *The Scientific Community* by Warren O. Hagstrom; and *Scientists: Their Psychological World* by Bernice T. Eiduson. I have also mined a good deal of ore from the works of Anne Roe, author of *The Making of a Scientist*. Finally, I want to thank Francis Bello, John T. Bonner, Walter Eckhart, Gerald Feinberg, and John Zabriskie for furnishing me with maps of the country that I set out to explore four years ago, and with introductions to its inhabitants. Needless to say, any faults that a reader may find in this report of my explorations are mine, not theirs.

Contents

Contents

Preface / A Brief Prospectus

NOT MANY YEARS AGO scientific research in the United States was for the most part a private activity. Except for those branches of science relevant to medicine, or to certain branches of industry and agriculture, science seemed as remote from the concerns of ordinary men as art or poetry. This notion was, of course, dispelled by Hiroshima and Nagasaki. People and their governments have come to look on science as a precious natural resource, on whose skillful exploitation the health, prosperity, and military might of nations all depend.

The awe that scientists now inspire, and the patronage they command, have inevitably changed the nature of their calling. They have become richer and more caught up in worldly affairs. A physicist may earn more than a United States senator, and scientists are continually being summoned to Washington to advise politicians on how to deal with smog, or missiles, or the high birth rate in Africa. One of the characteristic dilemmas that scientists now face is whether to regard such invitations as calls to duty, or as temptations to escape for a time, with some show of honor, the painful uncertainty and intellectual perils of scientific work.

Scientists have also been affected by changes in the technology of scientific investigation. In many branches of science enormous—and enormously expensive—instruments are required, together with the services of squads of engineers and technicians. As a result, more and more men who have been trained as scientists end up, by necessity or choice, as scientific administrators. The high cost of research has also made scientists more and more dependent on public patronage, forcing them to become involved in the kind of politics in which all citizens must engage if they want large sums of money from the government. The main business of science is still the pursuit of knowledge and understanding. But the way the pursuit is mounted, the rewards attendant on its success, and the temptations that beset the pursuer—all these have changed to an extent and in ways undreamed of when scientists now barely in their fifties were beginning their careers.

The aim of this book is to portray the scientific community in the United States: to convey a sense of what it is like to be a scientist in America in a time when science has become a form of established religion, and scientists its priests and ministers. Much of what I have written is based on published sources. But I have also drawn heavily on what I have been able to learn by questioning scientists themselves. Since 1964, I have talked at length with some one hundred and twenty-five scientists, constituting, in a very loose sense, a representative sample of the American scientific community. Among the people I interviewed were graduate students and postdoctoral trainees; scientists at big universities and scientists at small colleges; scientists who work with huge machines and direct the work of large teams of researchers and scientists who sit by themselves and think; scientists who work in industrial laboratories, scientists who work for the government, and scientists who run businesses of their own; scientific administrators and scientific politicians; applied scientists and scientists interested in events and domains almost unimaginably remote from the world we can see and touch and feel.

In general, I asked these people to tell me about their careers: about the choices they had made, and why, and how they felt about their work and its rewards. Some of the interviews were spread over two or three sessions, and lasted many hours. To encourage the people whom I interviewed to speak freely, I assured them I would not use their real names without their permission. Many of the people whom I have quoted in the pages that follow are therefore identified by names other than their own—a fact that I have indicated by italicizing such names the first time they appear. Where I have written at some length about a scientist's career, I have often changed not only his name but other identifying details as well.

It is hard to speak of oneself, even to a stranger and with the promise of anonymity, without striking poses. But most of the men and women with whom I talked seemed to feel an obligation to report on their lives as scientists with as much scientific objectivity as they could summon up, and on the whole they succeeded in summoning up a great deal. I was particularly impressed, and moved, by the honesty with which many of them talked about their fears of failing as scientists, and about the reality of failure itself.

A word is in order as to what kinds of scientists this book is about. My original intention, to which I have adhered, was to write mainly about mathematicians and people trained in what are often called the hard sciences. I was not sure what I should do about psychologists and economists and other social scientists. It seemed wrong to ignore them, and yet it soon became clear that unless I was prepared to stretch and mutilate them horribly I could not make them fit into the same bed that so nicely accommodated physicists, chemists, biologists, and other varieties of natural scientists. And so I decided to leave them out of the book, except for a brief Appendix in which I would explain *why* I had left them out, and say a few words about their status as demimondaines in the American scientific community. What I have to say elsewhere in the book should be taken as applying only to natural scientists.

I

On Becoming a Scientist

SCIENCE IS NOT a licensed profession, and to be counted as a scientist one need not be a Doctor of Philosophy. The compilers of the National Register of Scientific and Technical Personnel, a publication put out biennially by the United States government, define a scientist in a somewhat circular fashion as anyone who is eligible for membership in a recognized professional scientific society. Nearly 300,000 Americans meet this test, and around 200,000 of them have only a bachelor's or a master's degree. A few thousand have no degree at all.[1]

But a scientist without a Ph.D. (or a medical degree) is like a lay brother in a Cistercian monastery. Generally he has to labor in the fields while others sing in the choir. If he goes into academic life, he can hope to become a professor only at the kind of college or university where faculty members are given neither time nor facilities for research. He can, in principle, pursue his scientific interests on his own time, and there is nothing to keep him from applying to the government for a grant to pay for laboratory equipment and supplies. But for all the generosity with which the government now supports academic science, its patronage is limited mainly to scientists who have earned a doctorate, and are thereby supposed to have shown their ability to carry out scientific investigations on their own. Furthermore, because science is in many ways a highly social enterprise, in which scientists look to one another for suggestions, criticism, stimulation, and emotional support, even a scientist or mathematician who needs nothing more than a blackboard and chalk is at a disadvantage if he has no Ph.D. Barred from the institutions where significant scientific work is going on, he is forced to work in an isolation that may be fatal to his development as a scientist.

A young scientist with a bachelor's or a master's degree has little trouble, it is true, in getting a job in a government or industrial laboratory. But he will probably have to spend his time working on problems, or pieces of problems, that are assigned to him by other people and that are of more practical than scientific interest. Wherever he works, the prospects are slight that he will be given much autonomy and freedom. Having a Ph.D. or its equivalent—a medical degree plus postgraduate training in research—has become in fact, if not in law, a requirement for full citizenship in the American scientific community.

Americans who go to graduate school and become scientists tend to differ in one sociologically significant respect from those who become doctors or business executives or corporation lawyers. As a rule they come from poorer families. According to a study made in 1952, three out of five American business leaders are sons of business or professional men, and there have been reliable estimates that three out of four law students in the United States in the late 1950's, and two out of three medical students, were from "professional, managerial, proprietary families." By contrast, a 1960 survey indicated that something over half of the members of the American Chemical Society (including more than half of those with Ph.D.'s) had fathers who were manual or subprofessional white-collar workers.[2]

Other scientists do not necessarily resemble chemists in this respect. In 1948 *Fortune* collected information about the origins of some four thousand American scientists, and reported that while chemists seemed mostly to "come from small towns and *petit bourgeois* parents," physicists and mathematicians were more likely to have come from professional families and to have grown up "in an intellectual climate in which abstract ideas [were] not foreign." But children of upper-middle-class parents constituted only a small fraction of the scientists in *Fortune*'s sample. "The broadest generalization that may be made," the magazine noted, "is that scientists tend to come from lower income levels."[3] Two scholars, R. H. Knapp and H. B. Goodrich, reached much the same conclusion in a book called *Origins of American Scientists*, published in 1952. Knapp and Goodrich discovered that in the late 1920's and early 1930's, colleges like Kalamazoo and Hope and DePauw had been turning out three times as many scientists, in proportion to their size, as Harvard had, and five or six times as many as Yale.[4] One reason, they suggested, was that so many of the students at these colleges were boys from farms or small towns who, as one professor put it, "almost literally had a choice between the test tube and the plow."

Lately, however, more and more graduates of traditional rich men's colleges have been going into science.[5] At Harvard, for example, the number of students intending to become scientists rose from 6 percent of the graduating class in 1941 to 12 percent in 1965. This has led some people to assume that more and more sons of upper-middle-class fathers are choosing careers in science instead of in banking, medicine, or the law. Such a trend would not be surprising in view of the fact that science can now compete in terms of prestige (if not in terms of pay) with other leading professions. In 1947, when a poll was taken to determine how various occupations stood in the eyes of Americans, it showed scientists in a tie with congressmen for seventh place. A similar poll, taken in 1963, indicated that scientists had risen to third place in the public's esteem, and were outranked only by physicians and Supreme Court judges.[6]

But the fact is that today, as thirty years ago, young people who become scientists are much more likely to be sons or daughters of mechanics, clerks, or salesmen than of bankers, lawyers, or executives.[7] Few graduates of Groton or St. Marks or other fashionable boarding schools become physicists or biochemists, and the main reason why colleges like Harvard and Yale turn out so many more scientists than they used to is that they are getting a different kind of student.[8] Many more families can now afford to send their children away to expensive colleges, and a bright high-school graduate has a much wider choice of colleges than in the past even if his parents have no money at all to spare. A boy with a strong scientific bent who might once have worked his way through DePauw or Kalamazoo now wins a Merit Scholarship and goes to Harvard or Yale instead.

One reason why science, relatively speaking, is a poor man's game is that as a rule no ante is required. Unlike a medical or a law student, a student working for a Ph.D. in one of the sciences seldom has to borrow money or to rely on his wife or parents for support. He may work as a teaching assistant, and pay for his education by supervising laboratory sections in undergraduate science courses. Or he may work as a research assistant, which often means that he is getting paid for doing the research on which he will base his doctoral thesis. Or, if he is fortunate, he may have a fellowship, which has the advantages of being tax-free and of requiring nothing of the recipient except that he continue working for his doctorate. (Some fellowships also provide extra allowances for dependents.) Nine out of ten students in the natural sciences who have finished at least a year of graduate school, and who have started to work on their dissertations, are supported in one of these ways, earning, on the average, from $2,500 to $3,000 a year over and above their tuition fees.[9]

A great deal of this support now comes from the government. But long before the 1940's, when such support first became available, graduate students were being subsidized by the universities themselves. The theory was that scientists and scholars stood to earn so little money by their professions that it was unfair to make them pay for their education out of their own pockets. To be sure, graduate subsidies have not always been as generous as they are today. In the early 1930's, a graduate student in physics counted himself lucky if he had a fellowship that covered the cost of his tuition and left him $400 a year to live on. But, financially speaking, it has always been easier to earn a Ph.D. than a medical or a law degree.[10]

Two other things are worth noting about Americans who become scientists. A relatively large number are Jews, and very few are women. In 1954, *Fortune* asked a number of leading scientists to list the outstanding younger men in their fields, and sent questionnaires to one hundred and four of the scientists whose names appeared on the most lists. Eighty-seven responded, and twenty-four, or 29 per cent, gave their parents' religion as Jewish. This does not mean, of course, the 29 percent of all American scientists are Jews or of Jewish descent. But whereas only about 4 percent of the population of the United

States is Jewish, the proportion of scientists who are Jewish is probably at least 10 or 12 percent.[11] One reason for this is the high value that Jews have traditionally placed on skepticism, which is an essential element in the scientific way of looking at the world. By contrast, American Catholics have generally been brought up to look on skepticism as a threat to religious faith, and for this reason, among others, very few Catholics have become scientists. In *Fortune*'s group of eighty-seven outstanding young scientists, only four were from Roman Catholic families.

Another reason there are so many Jewish scientists is that there has been less anti-semitism in science than in many other callings. In the 1930's and 1940's, when medical schools were imposing strict quotas on the number of Jews they would accept, qualified Jewish students had little trouble getting into graduate schools of the arts and sciences. Moreover, in most fields of science Jews could have successful academic careers. Although social scientists and humanistic scholars who happened to be Jewish were seldom appointed to university professorships before World War Two, discrimination in the natural sciences was limited mainly to chemistry departments, whose members in many cases were regularly consulted by businessmen, and who tended to share the prevailing anti-semitism of their clients.[12] Today, discrimination against Jews in academic life is encountered mostly at third- and fourth-rate institutions that would be unlikely in any case to attract competent scientists. In industry, even though many big corporations still do not employ Jews as executives, there are few if any research laboratories in which Jewish scientists are not entirely welcome.[13]

By contrast, prejudice against women scientists is strong. Only 8 percent of the scientists listed in the 1966 National Register of Scientific and Technical Personnel were women. According to Bureau of the Census figures for 1959, women scientists earn only about two-thirds as much as men with equivalent training, and few women are professors at major universities or hold other important jobs in science. Many professors are loath to accept women as doctoral candidates. This is partly because they don't want to waste time on someone who may abandon science for motherhood. But there is another reason: a woman has little chance of achieving the kind of position that will reflect glory on the professor who has trained her. "Women scholars are not taken seriously and cannot look forward to a normal professional career," two sociologists reported in 1958 after a careful study of academic hiring and firing. They noted that universities like to hire prestigious scientists and scholars partly because their presence will make it easier to hire good people in the future. Women are discriminated against, they pointed out, "not because they have low prestige but because they are outside the prestige system entirely and for this reason are of no use to a department in future recruitment."[14]

To be successful as a scientist, it is important not only to have a Ph.D., but to have earned it at the right place. From the standpoint of rightness, American universities may be divided into three groups. The first is made up of those institutions to which the term "leading" may appropriately be applied. They include Chicago, Cal Tech, the University of California at Berkeley, Columbia, Harvard, Illinois, M.I.T., Michigan, Princeton, Stanford, Wisconsin, Yale, and perhaps two or three others.[15] These are the universities whose professors get the biggest research grants, publish the most scientific papers, serve on the most important government committees, win most of the scientific prizes, and are most likely to be acknowledged as leaders in their fields. Of the 36,000 persons who received doctorates in the natural sciences from American universities between 1960 and 1966, 29 percent received them from one of the twelve institutions I have named. Ranking just below these twelve are universities like Minnesota and Indiana and U.C.L.A., where scientists and scholars of international renown are also to be found, but not in such dense clusters as at Harvard or Berkeley. This group of institutions, whose number I have somewhat arbitrarily fixed at eighteen, awarded an additional 25 percent of all science doctorates in 1960–66. The remaining 46 percent were awarded by some one hundred and fifty other institutions, whose science departments, by and large, are staffed by scientists whose attainments have not been such as to bring them offers from major universities.[16]

This is not to say that first-rate scientists are to be found only at first-rate universities—or that there are no second-rate people at Berkeley and M.I.T. But from a graduate student's point of view, a minor university has serious disadvantages. One is that he will have a very limited choice of able professors from whom to select an adviser to guide him in doing research for his thesis. ("The direction I got from my professor was in almost every instance poor," I was told by a young biochemist who had earned his doctorate at a southern university. "It took me a year and a half to discover this. I got my degree, but my dissertation was very weak, and I didn't try to publish anything from it.") Another disadvantage is that the brightest students, like the brightest professors, tend to be found at the leading universities. Each year, for example, college seniors compete for several hundred graduate fellowships, awarded by the National Science Foundation, that can be used by the winners at any university they like, and in 1962 nearly half of the winners chose to use their fellowships at Harvard, the University of California, Princeton, and Stanford.[17]

The disadvantage of going to a graduate school where

the students tend to be mediocre is pointed up by Bernard Berelson in his study, *Graduate Education in the United States*. In 1959, Berelson questioned some 2,300 young scientists and scholars about their experiences as graduate students. Among other things, he asked them if they had learned "a great deal from one another." "About three-fourths said they had," he writes. "As a matter of fact, when I went on to ask: 'When you get right down to it, and taking everything into account, did you learn more from your fellow students or from your professors?' only about three-fourths said their professors. Most of the others said the score was about even."[18]

Anyway, it is a fact of academic life that a scientist can seldom rise above his academic origins. A chemist who has earned a doctorate at, say, Ohio State or Purdue, and whose work has impressed his faculty adviser, can reasonably aspire to a professorship at Pennsylvania State or Northwestern—but not at Harvard or Berkeley. This is partly for the reasons I have suggested, but also because the academic world is pervaded by snobbery. An excellent example of this snobbery has been given by the Washington correspondent of *The Reporter*, Meg Greenfield. Writing in 1963, Miss Greenfield described a conversation with a scientist, identified by her as a prominent government consultant, whom she had asked about the effects that nuclear tests might have on the Van Allen Radiation Belt. The Van Allen Belt is named after the man who discovered it, the physicist James A. Van Allen, and Miss Greenfield reported that the consultant "thought it relevant to point out" that Van Allen (who got his Ph.D. at the University of Iowa, and who heads Iowa's not particularly distinguished department of physics and chemistry) was "just a little man from Iowa." The question Miss Greenfield should have asked, he said, "was whether we would hire him at M.I.T." As Theodore Caplow and Reece J. McGee have said in their excellent study, *The*

Academic Marketplace, "[The] initial choice of a graduate school sets an indelible mark on the student's career. In many disciplines, men trained at minor universities have virtually no chance of achieving eminence. . . . Every discipline can show examples of brilliant men with the wrong credentials whose work somehow fails to obtain normal recognition."[19]

The intellectual voyage on which a prospective scientist embarks when he becomes a graduate student is quite unlike the journey that confronts the prospective doctor or lawyer. After the first year or so, his education is very much an individual affair. What he does and learns is determined partly by his own aptitudes and interests, and partly by the interests and style of the professor to whom he elects to apprentice himself for the last and most important stage of his formal education.

A revealing account of this experience was given to me by a young physicist named *Peter Coleman.* Coleman grew up in Brooklyn and went to Amherst, where he majored in physics. Like a number of undergraduates from other colleges, he spent the summer of his junior year working as a research assistant at the Woods Hole Oceanographic Institution, and by the spring of his senior year he had made up his mind that he wanted to do graduate work in geophysics —specifically in atmospheric physics. Speaking in a mildly depreciatory way, as though determined to claim no more than could be sustained in the face of a searching cross-examination, Coleman told me that his decision had not been made entirely on intellectual grounds. "The Ford Foundation was offering some pretty fat fellowships in meteorology," he said.

Coleman had done very well academically at Amherst, and was therefore in a position to take his pick of graduate schools. "In a way, M.I.T. was really the place to go," he said. "You had people there who really knew something about meteorology, people who were exploring the practical as well as the theoretical aspects. But I found that the meteorology department at M.I.T. was half a mile away from the physics department, and when I said I wanted to take a lot of physics courses they said, 'Well, you have to decide whether you want to be a physicist or a meteorologist.' I wasn't ready to make that choice."

Coleman then talked to a professor at another university, one which, like M.I.T., had a distinguished physics department, and which had just begun a small program of training and research in geophysics. "His attitude was just the opposite from M.I.T.'s," Coleman recalled. "He said their idea was that someone going into geophysics should be trained mainly in physics and mathematics. This left me the option of dropping geophysics if I found I didn't like it, without having to start all over again, so I decided to go there." He paused, and added, "I suppose this choice wasn't as intelligent and rational as I may have made it sound. I really had no data on the Great Men who were there. I asked some of my professors at Amherst, but all they would say was, 'Oh, yes, it's a pretty good place to go.' I liked the fact that it was in a big city, and I liked the fact that it was only a few miles away from the college where my fiancée would be finishing up the next year."

Before starting work on the research he will do for his thesis, a graduate student must typically spend a couple of years taking courses and preparing himself for a general examination in his field. Coleman was a little disillusioned by this phase of his graduate education. "At high school, I was like a lot of other people," he said. "I grubbed for marks. I thought when you got to college that stopped. I thought you'd sit around on the grass and discuss philosophy. Not at all. Everybody was driving like hell. Then I thought, 'Well, wait till you get to graduate school.' But when I got there, I found I just didn't have time to be a gentleman intellectual. Nobody actually told me I couldn't explore interesting byways, or speculate on larger things than the immediate problems put before me. But you could see it didn't pay. Like everybody else, I had to get my A's."*

In the spring of his second year, Coleman took an oral examination covering three broad areas of physics in which he had chosen to be questioned. "That was the biggest ordeal I had to face," he said. "I was scared. I had gotten a 'C' in one course. A 'C' is flunking at graduate school. Nothing like that had ever happened to me before. Before my oral I studied for a month solidly, twelve hours a day. Then on one horrible afternoon it was all over. I walked up and down the hall for a few minutes, and then the examiners—there were three of them—came out and shook my hand."

The physics department at the university where Coleman did his graduate work is a big one, and it is not unusual for forty or fifty students to be enrolled in a graduate course. Even after two years, Coleman said, many students know few if any professors. "After they pass their oral they tend to float around," he said. "They don't know who to ask to be their thesis adviser. So they ask the professor with the most prestige. V—— for instance, is a hotshot, a big name. He's at the top of the intellectual heap. K—— won a Nobel prize, but V—— is more appealing to hot-blooded young physicists. He has thousands—well, dozens—

* A number of young scientists with whom I talked did not share Coleman's feeling of having been forced to wear intellectual blinders while they were graduate students. A biologist who got his Ph.D. at the same university as Coleman said, "At graduate school you stop thinking about grades altogether. You stop committing things to memory. You start to think about problems, and about how they fit into the general context of science. You start reading the literature critically. This marks the point when you've begun to go somewhere."

of graduate students. But most of them seldom see him, and two years after they've been accepted by him they realize they're never going to get out of graduate school at the rate they're going, and they get someone else."

Coleman had no trouble settling on an adviser—there were only two full professors in geophysics, and in two years he had come to know both of them fairly well—or on the area in which he wanted to do his thesis. "In geophysics, the classes were small and chatty," he said. "Instead of final exams we had term papers, and these were a good source of ideas for thesis topics. By the time I took my oral I had a pretty good idea what research in various fields of geophysics was like. When I talked with my adviser we agreed quite quickly on a general topic. For about six months after my orals I just sort of wandered around this topic, and at the end we agreed that I really had a suitable experimental problem to go to work on."

Coleman said his relationship with his adviser had not been altogether satisfying. "He worked in a different lab, and actually at that time he was doing a good bit of theoretical work," he said. "I had a sort of distant relationship with him. I would see him once every week, or every two weeks, in a more or less formal way, and spend an hour or so explaining to him what I'd been doing. Your relationship with your professor is influenced by observing other students' relationships with him. I had seen my professor sort of bossing one of his students around. He tended to make snap judgments, and it was a little hard to convince him later that his snap judgment had been wrong. I was too proud to subject myself to this. I didn't want to reveal my ignorance, so I kept a lot of things from him. I would muddle through them on my own. When I saw him I would perform for him. I would try to think of all the clever little things I had done, and reel them off so I could be impressive. I didn't give him an entirely honest impression of my work. Maybe it wasn't too good an idea. Maybe I missed a lot of learning at my master's feet. I don't know."

When problems came up in the course of his research, Coleman said, he would ask other people working in the same laboratory—they were all graduate or postdoctoral students—for help. "I would talk with them about how to build a certain piece of electronic equipment, or about how to do anything. We swapped ignorances. We also spent a lot of time arguing about each other's work. Not just to be helpful, but to master the art of criticizing the other fellow's work and defending your own. My adviser's role was mainly to police me, to make sure I accomplished something, to make sure I was going in the right direction. He was there to see that I didn't bite off something too big, or something too trivial. But graduate students often don't get even that kind of guidance."

A few months after starting to work on his thesis, Coleman became discouraged. He put aside the experiment he had been working on, and began doing some nonexperimental research involving the use of a computer. "It was productive enough," he recalled, "but I really wasted a year, at the end of which I still had to make my original experiment work. I had fun doing these other things. It gave me a certain breadth. But the experiment was the core of my thesis, and I was really just putting it off while I fooled around with the computer. I got back to work on the experiment, and for a year I just cranked out the data. In the end, my thesis included some of the auxiliary stuff I had done, but it was no real advantage to me. I just took a year longer than I should have to get out of graduate school."

Three years after his preliminary oral, Coleman took his final examination, at which, in accordance with tradition, he was required to defend the validity and significance of his thesis. In general, this has become more of a ritual than an ordeal, since a candidate for a doctorate is usually permitted to go before the examining committee only when his adviser is satisfied that his thesis is acceptable—a judgment that the adviser's colleagues who sit on the examining committee are most unlikely to challenge. "It was very relaxed," Coleman said. "No one really examines you. They ask you to elaborate on certain points. The one question you can be sure they will ask is, 'Where does this fit into the bigger picture?' This wasn't too hard. There had been lots of seminars in geophysics to go to, some of them at other universities in the area. Even when I wasn't reading anything except an occasional novel and *Scientific American* I would go to these seminars. I wanted to keep up with my field so that when I got through graduate school I wouldn't be totally lost. When you're working on your thesis you have this fear that you're totally losing touch with your field."

Coleman would like to be a professor at a university where he could have a small research group, including graduate students, and where he would not have to do any more undergraduate teaching than he liked. When I talked with him, he was still at the university where he had got his degree a few months earlier, and where he was spending a year on a postdoctoral research fellowship. At the time we met, he was engaged in a common postdoctoral task: carving up his dissertation into publishable portions and sending them off to the appropriate journals. He said he expected this process to take about three months, and that he intended to start out then on a new line of research that would take him into a different area of atmospheric physics.

Reflecting on his five years as a graduate student, Coleman said, "It was intense at times, but once I'd passed my preliminary orals life was really pretty easy. I made a

pretense of being at the lab from nine to five. It was only a
pretense, though. I often played tennis in the morning or
afternoon. Sometimes I worked at night; sometimes I
didn't. The only flaw was that I wasn't getting anywhere
very fast. Occasionally I'd get pangs of conscience, and
there'd be a great spurt of activity. The last eight months
was one long spurt." Coleman went on to say that in some
ways he had found graduate school an anticlimax after
college. "There's less of the naïve excitement, that enormous enthusiasm for learning," he said. "Still, I like the
idea that now I know something about the ocean and the
atmosphere—and that I really *know* it, not in the wonderful, sophomoric way you know things at college. I like the
sense that now I'm professionally competent in my field.
But intellectually, it was not an exciting period. The rewards come mainly when you've finished."

Like Coleman, many scientists find their first two years
at graduate school rather harrowing. Students who have
gone to colleges that have weak science departments sometimes despair of catching up with students who have had
an opportunity, as undergraduates at big universities, to
take graduate-level courses in their junior and senior years.
At this time, too, a student may find that he has no taste, or
no aptitude, for work in the area of research that he has
chosen. "When I came here to Wisconsin I didn't know
there was such a thing as molecular biology," a young
biologist told me. He explained that he had majored in
physics at Yale, but that in the course of a year he had
spent at Oxford on a traveling fellowship he had decided
to switch out of the physical sciences. "But all I really
knew was that I was sick of physics," he said. "Biophysics
looked like the best way for me to get into biology, and
that's what I started out doing here at Wisconsin. I took a
wide variety of courses in my first year. Most of them were

pretty bad, and I was terribly depressed. That summer I took a course in cell physiology at Woods Hole, at the Marine Biological Laboratory, and the next spring I began doing some work in a laboratory here with a postdoctoral fellow who had a problem involving RNA control. I found I had just sort of fallen into molecular biology. I had to make up my mind to write off my first year entirely."

It is also quite common for physics students to decide after a year or so at graduate school that they had better become experimental physicists rather than theorists. "At Harvard, everybody wants to be a theorist," I was told by a physicist who got his degree there in 1960. "After all, the theorists are the great men in physics. When I was at Harvard, the department had an annual meeting just for the purpose of persuading students that it's a poor idea to become a theorist, because your chances of doing anything significant are pretty small. Some of us weren't hard to convince. It's very hard to do creative theoretical work on your own—it's hard enough just to understand the lectures. Of course, you can make up your mind that you're not going to be a great man, and find some pedestrian specialty. You locate some uncultivated theoretical field, and start cranking and producing. I decided to become an experimentalist." Sometimes, though not very often, a student will fail his preliminary oral examination and be flunked out. "In this department, what the orals are for is to give the department a chance to work you over and frighten you if they think you need frightening," a biology student told me. "Every once in a while they actually flunk someone—not often, just often enough to keep us honest."

But despite the uncertainties that can beset a student at this stage, in most cases the sternest test of his ability and determination comes when he has to prove that he can add something new to the world's store of scientific knowledge. In science, youth and inexperience are not necessarily a handicap. Older scientists are likely to be inhibited by knowing too many reasons why something cannot possibly be true, and discoveries of great significance have been made by graduate students. In 1925, to give just one example, the discovery that electrons spin like tops, which helped to answer some very basic questions about the structure and properties of atoms, was made by two students at the University of Leyden, Samuel Goudsmit and George Uhlenbeck, who did not finish their doctoral studies until two years later. Many students turn out work that has value at least to scientists who are at work on closely related problems in the same area of research.

But to be successful in basic research it is not enough to have a good mind. The researcher must be able to put up with long periods of groping and uncertainty, when he will not be sure what he is looking for or how to go about finding it. Many graduate students do well enough in their courses, but are seized with anxiety when confronted with a problem to which there is no known solution—and which may prove, given the existing state of knowledge, to be to all intents and purposes insoluble. Berelson quotes a physicist who told him that "the practice these days . . . is to give the student a dissertation topic not really at the frontier of knowledge but in the area just this side of it. A topic at the frontier would be both too difficult and too uncertain."[20]

Some students, however, are baffled even by relatively safe and tidy experiments. A few of these hang on as graduate students for six or seven years without producing a thesis, and leave at last to take a job in industry or in a government laboratory, or to teach at a college. Others quit after a year or two and then come back to graduate school after a spell of teaching and have another try. Still others stick it out, relying on their advisers to lead them step by step through the trackless wild that separates them from a Ph.D. "The students who aren't very good think you're a kind of magician," a professor of biology at an eastern university told me. "They see you doing research, and they try to see what it is you do that makes it work. But *they* can't make it work. They become dependent on you. It's terrible. In the end, they get their degree and say to themselves, 'Thank God, I'm never in my life going to have to do research again.'" Students like this, the professor added, often end up happily teaching at colleges that require a faculty member to have done enough research to get a Ph.D., but that do not insist that he keep on doing it.

In general, scientists who teach at universities are a little more enthusiastic about their doctoral students than these remarks might suggest. There are brilliant students as well as dependent and despairing ones. "The really good ones keep me educated," I was told by this same biologist. "They try things I would never have thought of trying. They constantly prod me to be on my toes. Of course, the ones who are really good don't hide the fact that they think you're an awful jerk. They think you're senile. It's very bracing."

Even students who are less than brilliant can be assets to a professor. A scientist as a rule can effectively supervise a piece of doctoral research only if the student is working in the particular area in which the professor himself is working. In practice, a doctoral thesis is most often a collaborative effort. The professor furnishes the basic idea— in many branches of the natural sciences, a student selects his thesis topic only in the sense that he has his choice of several possibilities suggested by his adviser—and guides the research. The student builds equipment, makes observations and calculations, analyzes the data he accumulates, and writes the thesis. Later, the job of translating the thesis into the more succinct form required for publication in a scientific journal may be done by either the student or the professor. Regardless of which one actually writes the paper, it will ordinarily carry the names of both as joint authors. The dean of an unidentified graduate school, a chemist by training, wrote Berelson that "in the case of many a professor in distinguished institutions, the major scholarly work of the professor is simply the summation of the original work which graduate students have done in collaboration with him. Only occasionally does a professor of chemistry write an article which is not in collaboration with a graduate student."[21]

Collaboration can be exhilarating to the student as well as beneficial to the professor. A physicist with whom I talked recalled with obvious pleasure the work he had done as a candidate for a doctorate at a leading eastern university. He and another student had jointly performed an experiment suggested to them by their faculty adviser, a well-known physicist who was soon afterward to win a Nobel prize. "What Charley did was to contribute a vision, something for which even the basic principles hardly existed," the physicist said. "From his point of view, he had two graduate students who could develop this idea. We had the benefit of his background and his experience. He was very interested in this project. He spent half an hour a day talking with us. He didn't exploit us; he threw in so many ideas that I really had an unusual opportunity. Some professors do exploit students. They develop some big, elaborate piece of equipment and then set their students to work measuring things with it. It was different with Charley. He would propose ideas and solutions for us to try. It was very exciting."

At its best, the graduate training that scientists get at American universities is unsurpassed anywhere in the world. The virtual destruction of German science by Hitler, the migration of many leading European scientists to

America, the generosity with which the United States government has supported basic scientific research—all these have transformed the quality of American science. Twenty-five years ago the United States was still importing much of its basic science, and as recently as the 1930's the best young American scientists often finished their education abroad. Today European students come to American universities for graduate or postgraduate study in the sciences as Americans once went to Göttingen or Cambridge. "The Americans . . . are proving that you can be rich and clever," John Davy, the science correspondent of the London *Observer*, wrote wistfully not long ago. "The enormous, wealthy campuses of Stanford, Berkeley, the Massachusetts Institute of Technology, Harvard and others are not only rolling in dollars—they are fizzing with intellectual excitement."[22]

But graduate education in the sciences in the United States is by no means uniformly excellent. Some professors are incompetent, and some are too busy with other things to bother much with their graduate students. Berelson asked the 2,300 young scientists and scholars to whom he sent questionnaires whether they thought that "one basic trouble with graduate school is that faculty members do not consider the students as their main responsibility (as compared to their own research, consultation and service jobs, administration, etc.)." Half of them said they agreed with this statement—as did half of some 1,800 members of graduate faculties to whom Berelson put the same question.[23]

Perhaps the most serious thing wrong with graduate education in the sciences is that the student too often is treated as a peon. Instead of being initiated into the art of doing independent research, he is set to work on tedious but essentially trivial tasks whose accomplishment will contribute mainly to the reputation of his professor. This sort of exploitation is by no means unknown in the humanities, but in recent years it has been particularly common in the natural sciences. When Berelson suggested to young scientists and scholars that "major professors often exploit doctoral candidates by keeping them as research assistants too long, by subordinating their interests to departmental or the professor's research programs, etc.," 46 percent of the natural scientists in his sample said they agreed, and only 34 percent disagreed. In the case of both the social scientists and the humanists the vote went the other way.[24]

The exploitation of graduate students in the sciences has been fostered by a huge increase in the size and cost of the apparatus used in certain important fields of research. The most striking example is the new linear electron accelerator at Stanford University. This instrument, which is being used to study the particles produced when electrons traveling at very high velocities collide with atomic nuclei, is two miles long, cost $120 million to build, and has an operating staff of nearly a thousand persons. The effect such instruments have on the training of graduate students has troubled many people, including a number of leading scientists who attended a conference on basic research held at Princeton in 1960. The published report of their discussions notes disapprovingly that "a university with large-scale research projects (for example, the multibillion-volt accelerators) is likely to throw the senior graduate students into the gap between the scientific faculty and the machine-shop personnel." The report goes on to say, "A graduate student assigned to work on such a 'big machine' may become little more than a technician for that particular machine. The research that earns him his doctorate will be just a variant of a certain kind of experiment with the machine and he will never have built a single apparatus for himself."[25]

Such exploitation is not confined to fields, like high-

energy physics, in which the technology of research tends
to rule out truly independent work by graduate students.
(The Princeton conferees conceded that unfortunately it is
not practical to let a graduate student putter around on his
own with an accelerator.) Since World War Two, more
and more research has been done by teams, even when no
big machines are being used. The evolution and character
of this new style of doing scientific work will be considered
in Chapter V, but something should be said at this point
about its effect on graduate students. One of the ways in
which the government subsidizes the training of scientists
is by making grants to professors, or contracting with them,
for research in which they will be assisted by their students. But in deciding whether to support a particular
project, a government agency may be more concerned with
its relevance to some practical aim—the development of a
more efficient rocket fuel, for example—than with the educational benefits that may or may not accrue to graduate
students who will work on the project. In some kinds of
research, as in the manufacture of refrigerators or automo-
biles, high output depends on an appropriate division of
labor. And the professor who likes the idea of running a
big shop, in which his students will be assigned to positions on an assembly line, can now quite easily find money
with which to indulge this taste.

It is true that universities officially take a dim view of
professors who use graduate students as semiskilled labor-
ers. But universities are always short of money, and a dean
or president will be most reluctant to veto a research project, no matter how pedestrian, that is going to bring in
enough money, say, to pay summer salaries to three members of the faculty and provide research assistantships for
half a dozen doctoral candidates. Universities do usually
draw the line at accepting projects that are of interest only
to the government agency that is footing the bill, and not

to the professor who will be running the show. But professors can have surprisingly catholic tastes. As Charles V. Kidd observes in *American Universities and Federal Research*, "Many faculties . . . appear to have interests which encompass routine material testing, accumulation of data of little general scientific interest, and similar enterprises."[26]

In general, it is the less promising students who have to earn their Ph.D.'s by working on a scientific assembly line. The best students, as I have said, tend to go to the best universities, and these may be defined as universities where, by and large, the professors are good enough so that they don't have to set up data factories in order to get research grants. Also, the best students often have fellowships, and therefore are not tempted, as less fortunate students often are, to select a faculty adviser whose main attraction is that he has research assistantships to hand out.*

As for the mediocre student, it can be argued that a professor is doing him a favor by letting him earn a Ph.D. simply by being industrious and docile. There are now a great many good jobs in which scientific training is needed, but which do not require the capacity for doing significant

---

* A survey in 1960 by a member of the Princeton faculty, William G. Bowen, indicated that one out of six graduate students in the natural sciences at Princeton had picked his field of research at least partly for financial reasons. "The availability of funds for particular types of research which support particular points of view is a great attraction to one dependent upon financial support," one student commented. "I have been sucessfully tempted." Bowen reported, "The Physics Department has simply refused to allow students to use work done on sponsored research contracts for their own theses. Research assistantships are awarded to first and second year students who do not have fellowship funds. Third year (post-generals) students without fellowship funds are awarded part-time *teaching* assistantships, so as to avoid any danger of conflicts between a man's research interests and his employment obligation to the department or to a Government sponsor."[27]

research on one's own. But even in jobs such as these, the quality of a man's training counts, and one common criticism of the way government funds are dispensed is that professors are permitted to build research machines that turn out, along with streams of inconsequential research papers, streams of scientists who are poorly equipped even for jobs in which originality and imagination are not essential.

Although possession of a Ph.D. is supposed to signify that a scientist has learned his trade as a researcher, it is now very common for young scientists to continue in a quasi-student status for a year or two after they get their doctorates. Postdoctoral research fellowships are not especially new, but before World War Two they were available to no more than a few dozen people each year. Now there are so many, and so many jobs as research associates that are the equivalent of research fellowships, that one often finds as many postdoctoral as graduate students in a university laboratory.

Older scientists as a rule are very happy to take on postdoctoral students. The post-doc, as he is sometimes called, is like an advanced graduate student in that he does research under the general direction of an older man. But he usually needs much less direction, and he can therefore be much more helpful to an experienced scientist who is eager to see his work pushed forward as rapidly as possible. "Taking graduate students—I consider that a duty," a molecular biologist told me. "From the point of view of getting research done, it's much better to have postdoctoral people. You waste a hell of a lot of time with graduate students. They keep asking, '*Now* what shall I do, Daddy?' " Postdoctoral trainees can have the further advantage of serving a professor as a middleman in his dealings with his graduate students. A graduate student may get day-today guidance (and encouragement) not from his faculty adviser, but from a postdoctoral student with whom his adviser has suggested that he collaborate. Having postdoctoral trainees around, as Berelson points out, also permits members of a department to look over prospective recruits without having to give them three-year appointments as instructors or assistant professors.[28]

For young scientists themselves, a year or two of postdoctoral study and research has many attractions. For some it is a chance to make up for what they didn't learn in graduate school. "The present rapid growth of the postdoctoral fellowship idea," a graduate dean told Berelson, "is, at least in part, a direct result of many of our Ph.D.'s having been trained in too-large groups, in overextended graduate departments, and under 'team research' circumstances."[29] For scientists whose graduate training has been good, the chief advantage of doing postdoctoral research —apart from the fact that major universities usually insist that junior faculty members come to them with this sort of seasoning—is that it gives them a couple of years in which they can put all their effort into research.[30] If a man is fortunate, this is time enough for him to establish, by the number and quality of the papers that he publishes, a sufficient reputation so that when he does begin to teach at a university he will be in a position to compete effectively for research grants. A postdoctoral fellowship can also be a relatively tranquil interlude between the pressures and intellectual restrictions of life as a graduate student, and the competition and distractions of life as an assistant professor. Many scientists go abroad, not because the training they get will necessarily be better than they would get in the United States, but because a postdoctoral fellowship gives them a chance to travel—often for the first time in their lives. "I didn't have any illusions about doing important work in Germany," I was told by a physicist who recently spent eighteen months as a postdoctoral fellow there. "It was the first time my wife and I had ever had any money or been anywhere. The fellowship paid about twice as much as I'd been getting as a graduate student. The last half of the time I was over there I buckled down and worked like hell. But for the first nine months we mainly traveled around and had a ball."

Some men use their postdoctoral interlude to broaden themselves by learning new techniques. Others use it to establish themselves in what they believe to be a more fertile sector of the field in which they were trained at graduate school. Occasionally a student will change to an altogether different discipline, typically because he wants to get into an exciting new field that is opening up. One scientist with whom I talked told me that after getting a Ph.D. in physical chemistry in the late 1940's he had decided to switch fields, and had gone to Cal Tech as a postdoctoral fellow to study molecular biology under Max Delbruck, a biologist who had himself started out as a physicist. "Those were the most formative years of my life," he said. "It was like being born again. There was a fantastic collection of people there. Everybody was interested in everyone else. We all went to each other's seminars. Sometimes fifteen or twenty of us would go camping together. Delbruck's group was like Niels Bohr's laboratory in Copenhagen. Molecular biology really took shape in this country then, and the shape it took was largely the work of Delbruck."

Few scientists, of course, have the good fortune to play a part, at the outset of their careers, in an event of such historic significance as the founding and early development of molecular biology. But for many men the years they spend in postdoctoral training are an enormously exhilarating time, when they first gain confidence in their own powers and begin to form their own style as scientists. In a report urging the government to increase its support of chemical research, a group of eminent American chemists recently described postdoctoral study in these enthusiastic terms: "At this level, a student . . . is usually in a stimulating environment, at a time in his life when he has great energy and motivation, when he is reasonably free to exercise his own professional judgment, and when he is least burdened by additional responsibilities. The momentum he achieves in this period is likely to determine the direction and extent of his future career."[31]

Even scientists too young to be suspected of middle-aged nostalgia often speak rapturously of their own years as postdoctoral students. A theoretical physicist now in his early thirties, who got his doctorate at Harvard and then went as a postdoctoral fellow to the Institute for Advanced Study in Princeton, considers the time he spent there the happiest of his life. "There were twenty or twenty-five other young physicists there," he told me. "It was a fairly competitive group—people were very eager to establish a reputation—and the atmosphere was very highly charged. At the Institute, for the first time you were on your own. You had to think up things to work on and work them out. But there were all those other people to talk to. Many days we would talk physics more or less continuously all day long. Literally." After a year at the Institute for Advanced Study, and before he became an assistant professor at Berkeley, he spent a year as a research associate at Brookhaven National Laboratory on Long Island. "At the Institute I had been one of a group of five or six people of something like equal ability," he said. "At Brookhaven there were several other young physicists, but I guess I would have to say I was the best of the group. I spent much less time talking with my contemporaries than at the

Institute. I published six or seven papers that year. This was the time when I rounded off the corners of my approach to physics. It was a very productive year. But when I was at the Institute I thought it was as close to paradise as one could come on earth."

II

Science for the
Sake of Science

I N THE COURSE of testifying at a Congressional
hearing on the state of American science and technology, the
well-known physicist Edward Teller recently described what
he said had been a "shocking experience." He explained that
he was currently trying to recruit students for graduate training in applied science—training, that is, in the translation of
scientific knowledge into new devices and new technologies, a
pursuit to which Teller himself has devoted the greater part
of his career. "I interviewed last Saturday and Sunday
twenty-four promising students at M.I.T.," he said. "Apart
from the technical questions, we persistently raised the question: 'When you get your doctor's degree, what will you then
want to do?' Twenty-two out of the twenty-four answered: 'I
want to continue in the academic career. I will not take an industrial job. I will try as best I can to continue in pure research and teaching.' " Teller added, "For some reason or
other our most talented people are brought up in a way which
induces them to turn up their noses at anything that is
practical."[1]

Teller's observation is perhaps misleading in one respect.
Able scientists who are primarily occupied in doing basic

44

research, which may be defined as research undertaken without any specific practical aim in view, often take time off to do jobs that involve the application of scientific knowledge rather than its extension. Some such jobs, mainly those that involve consulting with industry, are taken on because they pay well. Others are taken on because scientists feel a sense of obligation to the government and to their fellow men, because it can be comforting to tackle (and solve) a practical problem when one's own research seems to be getting nowhere, or simply because of a reluctance to see a job botched by engineers. "Engineers are essentially conservative," an experimental physicist told me. "They will use existing technological means to solve a problem. But they won't devise new means, or use them in novel ways, which is what experimental scientists are good at doing." Over the past eighteen years, this particular scientist, who considers basic research his real trade, has worked on the development of the hydrogen bomb, devised a method for improving communications between military aircraft, given advice on the design of long-distance radar warning systems and of intercontinental missiles, invented the fan-jet engine (he concedes that someone else invented it first), and helped draw up plans for enforcing a ban on the testing of nuclear weapons and for controlling insect pests.

But this is only another way of saying that, as Teller complains, the ablest and most imaginative scientists in the United States as a rule prefer to concentrate on basic research. The full-time applied scientist may have to spend much of his time on problems that are set for him by his employers, and that may be of little intrinsic scientific interest. By contrast, the basic researcher is free, in principle, to work only on what interests him—a freedom he shares with artists, poets, and people who inherit money. Basic research also has the fascination of being a game in which victory—the discovery of a new relationship or the formulation of a new law or concept—confers on the victor the gratifying sense of having changed the universe.

In this chapter I shall try to convey, by means of biographical sketches, an idea of the terms by which this game is played in America today, and of the people who play it. The subjects are scientists who are engaged mainly or exclusively in basic research—or were at the time I talked with them about their careers. Two of them are physicists, one is a biologist, one is a chemist, and one is an astronomer.

Irving Edelstein, a poised and articulate man in his very early thirties, is a theoretical physicist whose choice of a career was dictated by an early, potent, and sustained curiosity about the underlying structure of the physical world. He grew up in New York—his father was a reporter for a Yiddish-language newspaper—and at ten he was reading books on chemical theory. At twelve he began to teach himself physics, and at the Bronx High School of Science, where he went when he was fourteen, he learned less science from his teachers than from a few precocious classmates. After graduation, he entered Columbia, where he majored in physics, cultivated an interest in philosophy, and got his bachelor's degree in three years. In 1955 he went to Harvard as a graduate student.

For his dissertation, Edelstein chose a problem in particle physics, the branch of physics that deals with the behavior and properties of the subnuclear particles that have been discovered in such profusion during the past thirty years. Because particle physics is concerned with the most fundamental questions about the nature of matter, it has tended to attract the most gifted theorists, and Edelstein at first felt overpowered by the brilliance of his faculty adviser. "He seemed so much better than me, so very much better," he recalls, "that I wondered if I could ever possibly do the same sort of things he could do. But I wanted to work in theoretical physics—I was always interested in *knowing* things rather than doing them. After a while I decided I could do pretty well at it." Edelstein's confidence was justified. After getting his Ph.D. in 1958, he spent two years as a postdoctoral research fellow, during which time he published about a dozen papers, and was then hired as an assistant professor at an eastern university that is one of the main centers of experimental work in particle physics. Two years later, at the very early age of twenty-eight, he was made an associate professor and given lifetime academic tenure.

Given his ability and tastes, Edelstein's circumstances are close to ideal. His salary, including the $3,000 he can count on being paid each summer out of research funds provided by the Atomic Energy Commission, comes to about $17,000 a year, and Edelstein, who is a bachelor, feels no compulsion to take on outside jobs in order to make money. At the present stage of his career, he has no administrative duties and serves on no faculty committees. He teaches only one course each semester. Recently he has been giving a graduate course in particle theory. But he has also taught a less advanced course, in which undergraduate as well as graduate students were enrolled, and one year he taught, at his own request, a course for liberal arts majors of the type sometimes known as Physics for Poets. He has three graduate students working on theses under his supervision; he sees them each about once a week.

Most of the time Edelstein is free to think or read or write about particle physics, or to talk about physics with other physicists. The experimental data in which particle physicists are interested are produced by bombarding atomic nuclei with protons or other particles to which very

high energy has been imparted, and many of the people
with whom Edelstein talks do experiments with big accelerators. During the academic year he spends a couple of
days each month at Brookhaven National Laboratory, on
Long Island, where one of the most powerful of these
machines is located. From time to time he goes to California to talk with physicists at Stanford and Berkeley. In
the summer, he is likely to spend a month at Brookhaven,
and another month or so at a summer institute, usually
held in Europe, where he will lecture on his work and have
a chance to talk with leading physicists from other countries. As a rule the government pays his travel bills, but
recently he also traveled extensively at the expense of the
Sloan Foundation. "They just sent me a letter asking if I
could use a certain amount of money," Edelstein says. "I
said I could." He used the money to go around the world,
pausing for a month in Japan, six weeks in India, and five
months at Cambridge, where he gave some lectures on
physics to graduate students, and spent a lot of time thinking about philosophical problems.

Edelstein publishes four or five scientific papers a year,
and in the opinion of other physicists in the United States
and abroad, who are the real judges of his work rather
than his faculty colleagues, their quality is such as to place
him among the leading younger theorists in his field. To
sustain such a reputation it is necessary to keep on having
good ideas—and to have them before other people do.
Edelstein says that he worries very little, however, about
the chance of being beaten out by competitors, a possibility that haunts many scientists in fiercely competitive
fields like particle physics, in which half a dozen people
may be trying to crack the same problem. "Somebody
who's important in my field might succeed in doing something I'd been trying to do for a year," Edelstein says.
"Well, my reaction would be, okay, fine, I'll go on and do

something else." One might be inclined to attribute such generosity to the fact that Edelstein has a secure job and an established reputation. But his serenity seems to spring from a deeper source, an unshakable belief in his own creative power. Once, soon after getting his doctorate, he wrote a paper that was accepted for publication, and before it appeared in print he received a copy of a paper by a Russian physicist who had dealt with a very similar problem in very much the same way. To a young scientist trying to make his way in the academic world but having less confidence in himself than Edelstein, this could be a hard blow. "I felt sort of pleased that someone else had thought it was an interesting thing to do, too," Edelstein says.

Edelstein expends his intellectual energies on other things besides thinking about the structure and laws of matter. For a while he belonged to an organization of scientists, known as the Jason Group, that meets periodically under government auspices to discuss ways of enhancing the security of the United States, and of improving its military capabilities. He is no longer convinced, as he once was, that scientists have an obligation to lend a hand, when asked, to the military establishment. But he has thought seriously of involving himself in the space program. This is not because he believes the program is likely to yield any very big scientific dividends, but because he thinks that projecting man into interplanetary space, like building a cathedral, is a noble undertaking, and one that the United States is especially well qualified to bring off successfully. "If I decided to go to work on Apollo it would be on something *not* connected with particle physics," he says. "I could solve things. I would put particle physics aside for a bit."

As a boy, Edelstein read a lot of science fiction, and not long ago he got together a group of scientists, philosophers, and historians to discuss questions of a sort that science fiction writers deal with more often than scientists. "We asked ourselves, What do we do when we know how to manipulate genes?" Edelstein told me. "What if we can —and do—make truly intelligent machines, machines that can even do physics better than people can? What effect will this have on human psychology, on the way that men view themselves? In our discussions we took it for granted that we would soon be able to do these things, and asked ourselves, Do we *want* to do them? What are the implications? We pursued the implications of extending the human life-span by a factor of a hundred or so. What kind of society would we have if people lived long enough so that a man could build a cathedral by himself in his own lifetime? Would there be room at the top in society if people lived ten thousand years? What kind of marriage customs would we have?"

Edelstein is writing a book in which he is exploring some of these questions. He has also contributed articles to professional philosophical journals, and he occasionally writes poetry, though not (so far) for publication. One of his poems, written when he was twenty-four, is called "Passion" and reads:

> It is no easy thing to break
> Habits of the life of reason,
> To fling the garment off, and wake
> The dormant passions in their season.
> And yet the effort must be made
> Or else I leave a sphere untried.
> The fact of feeling is not stayed
> By being endlessly denied.

Henry Guthrie, a forty-five-year-old professor of biology at a leading private university, is something of an anomaly in American science. He was born into a family that was both cultivated and well-to-do. As a young boy, he went to pri-

vate schools in New York and in Switzerland, and for two
years he and an older brother were tutored at home. When
he was eleven he spent a lot of time studying the ducks in
St. James Park in London, and thought of becoming an
ornithologist. His father, who was taking a breather at the
time between a business and a diplomatic career (he later
became a successful novelist), discouraged this idea. He
said that ornithology was a potty, amateurish pursuit, and
that if Henry wanted to be a scientist he should be a biologist. After reading H. G. Wells's *The Science of Life*,
Henry found himself for once in complete agreement with
his father. His family spent its summers in New Hamp-
shire, and he began taking long walks and returning with
bags full of plant specimens, which he would dissect and
examine under a secondhand microscope his parents had
given him. "My interest in biology was awfully intense,"
Guthrie says. "I remember reading about Darwin and Huxley, and hero-worshipping them. Of course, my judgment
wasn't as good as it is now. I thought Huxley was a greater
man than Darwin. Now I think Huxley would make an
excellent university president."

At fourteen Guthrie went to Exeter, where he found
that his passion for biology gave him no standing at all
among the esthetes and wits and intellectuals of the school.
"I was automatically put in the same category as the dull
tools who put radios together," he says. "My mother was
really a *fierce* intellectual, and my father was very well
read. He was an expert on everything. I had a tremendous
amount of information about the arts, about painting and
literature. At Exeter I was taken into the Lantern Club, not
because of my interest in science, but because I had been
brought up in what I suppose you would call a highly
cultured background. My mother thought science was perfectly okay, but she took the position that an interest in
science didn't excuse you from going to museums and con-

certs and reading tremendously. I myself felt a certain con-
tempt for the kind of student who could only put a radio
together." In 1937, Guthrie entered Harvard, where his
situation was much as it had been at Exeter. He took all
the biology courses that were open to undergraduates, but
found most of his friends among those whom a member of
a later Harvard class has described as "students . . . in
whom most components of the Protestant ethic are cor-
roded; who subordinate a pragmatic to an esthetic attitude; and to whom science is something for less exalted
souls."

Guthrie graduated in 1941, and after spending a summer in Panama, where he had gone with the intention of
collecting certain kinds of fungi but instead had spent his
time looking at birds and reading Proust and Dreiser, he
returned to Harvard as a graduate student. He was in-
ducted into the Army eighteen months later, and spent the
next three years in an Army Air Force laboratory worrying
about matters such as the fungal deterioration of military
clothing and equipment. In 1946 he went back to Harvard
and started work on his thesis. "This was tremendously
satisfying," he recalls. "I had the eureka phenomenon—
well, maybe not quite that, but I tried an experiment that
really worked. As a matter of fact, it was probably one of
the better things I've done. But when I got my Ph.D. I was
depressed. At my examination I was sitting there all sensitive and prickly, and I had a feeling the examiners didn't
understand what I had done or why it was significant.
They didn't really seem terribly interested."

In 1947 Guthrie left Harvard to become an assistant professor at the university where he has been a member of the
faculty ever since. From the start he enjoyed teaching. "It
has been a tremendous help to me in getting my ideas
organized," he says. "For years I couldn't write anything
without giving a lecture on it first." As it happened, it

was many years before he had anything to write about that was of as much significance as the experiment he had done for his dissertation. But he was turning out good, solid work, and in 1951 he was made an associate professor and given tenure. Seven years later, while he was spending a sabbatical year at the University of Edinburgh, he wrote the chairman of his department that a chair was soon to become vacant at Edinburgh, and that he was thinking of putting in for it. Guthrie was thereupon promoted to full professor with shocking (but gratifying) celerity.

Guthrie's research has for many years been financed mainly by the National Science Foundation. Each year he writes a letter in which he very briefly describes the work that has been done in his laboratory in the past, and lists some of the things he hopes to do in the near future. In return, he has been getting about $15,000 a year. About $2,000 of this goes to the university for overhead expenses. The rest pays Guthrie's so-called summer salary, provides him with the services of a laboratory assistant, and buys supplies and equipment for Guthrie and for the other people who work in his laboratory—three or four graduate students, an equal number of undergraduates doing senior research projects, and sometimes a postdoctoral student as well. Fifteen thousand dollars a year is not much as research grants go. Government support of university professors doing experiments in high-energy physics has recently averaged around $160,000 per professor per year, and even in biology some professors have research budgets of $100,000 a year or more. Guthrie's requests to the National Science Foundation are as modest as they are because he deliberately avoids problems that require, or seem to require, expensive instruments for their solution. "My idea is not to be involved with machines," he says. "If I decide on Tuesday that I'm going about something the wrong way, I want to be able to start going about it in a different way on

Wednesday with a clear conscience. I don't want to feel
guilty because there's a big, new, expensive instrument
standing in the corner that I haven't even unpacked yet
and that I no longer have any use for."

A scientist is judged by other scientists almost entirely
by the number and quality of the papers that he publishes
in which he describes the results of an experiment, reports
on things that he has observed or measured, or suggests
solutions to specific theoretical problems. A successful scientist may also turn out an occasional review article summarizing and discussing recent developments in his field,
and he may write an advanced textbook. But he is unlikely
to do much writing of any other kind.

Guthrie, however, is a prolific author. He spends his
summers in Nova Scotia, dividing his days about equally
between writing and fishing for salmon, and this regimen
has so far produced five books. Three of them deal very
broadly with the growth and development of organisms,
the processes that he studies experimentally in his laboratory. "Besides doing experimental work, which is tremendous fun, I think I have a responsibility to show how the
work I do fits into the larger scheme of things," Guthrie
says. "In biology there are very few books of this sort. The
usual way to summarize a field is in a textbook. But in a
textbook you wouldn't hook up ideas in new ways, which is
what I have tried to do. You would try to hook them up in
clear and conventional ways." The first of Guthrie's books
has been translated into several languages, and has been
widely read by students who want to know what the field
of developmental biology is all about. When it was published in 1952, Guthrie took the conventional view that
inasmuch as it contained no new facts, it properly belonged in the category of teaching, not of research. He is
now inclined to think that this book, and the two others
like it that he has written, serve a purpose closely related

to what he does in his laboratory. By providing other investigators with conceptual maps, Guthrie feels, these books may affect the course of experimental work in his particular field of biology at least as much as his own experiments will.

Guthrie has also written two books that he refers to, like Graham Greene, as entertainments. In these, he has dealt with biological ideas in a nontechnical way. Many scientists tend to the view that a man who writes books of this kind is either frivolous or intellectually bankrupt. "But not all of my colleagues frown on this sort of thing," Guthrie says tolerantly. "Some of them say they're actually glad I wrote them. They say there's a need for such books. Of course they always add they wouldn't touch one with a ten-foot pole themselves."

Like a great many scientists, Guthrie would rather have nothing to do with administration. This has not been easy. "I've had trouble with this ever since I was a graduate student," he says. "People at Harvard had the impression that I was a sort of smooth talker and operator. This was wrong; no one could have been more genuinely interested in biology than I was. Yet the fact that I could be coherent on my feet made people look down on me a little. I had a haunting feeling that people thought I was going to end up being a dean."

Guthrie has avoided this fate. But a few months after I talked with him about his career I saw him again, and this time he was sitting in a big office, explaining to someone over the phone that there were certain forms he should fill out if he was sure that he was going to run over his research budget. When he hung up he explained that he had agreed to be chairman of his department for three years. "If ever there was a case of someone not wanting to make a career out of this, it's me," he said. "But what can I do? If I want this department to keep on being the kind of place it has been, I can't be completely irresponsible about how it is run. I try to spend my mornings in the lab, and at the moment things are booming along. That's because I haven't really needed any new ideas so far this fall. If I'd had to work up a new approach, I'd have been sunk. Maybe by spring I'll have things straightened out here, and I'll be able to do some creative work instead of just following through on things. The trouble is that when I leave the house in the morning and walk over here I'm not thinking about what I'm going to do in the lab. I'm thinking about money."

James Cantelli, an experimental physicist, belongs among those scientists whom Einstein once compared to athletes. "To this class of men," Einstein wrote, "science is a kind of sport in the practice of which they exult, just as an athlete exults in the exercise of his muscular prowess."[2] A dark, slightly built man of thirty-one, who wears half-rimmed glasses and neat, dark suits, Cantelli is not professionally concerned with questions about the underlying structure of the universe of the kind that engross physicists like Edelstein. His work is in nonlinear optics, a field in which the theoretical techniques are well developed, but in which Cantelli has ample scope for exercising his prowess as an experimenter. "In what I'm doing, one discovers many new phenomena, phenomena that are relatively easily understood," he says. "The fun involved is in seeing new and, in a way, beautiful arrangements of things no one has seen before."

Cantelli is a New Englander by birth. At the age of ten, with the encouragement and help of his father, an electrician who later became a professional magician, he began doing experiments with spark coils. He got his bachelor's degree at the University of Massachusetts, where he took courses in mathematics, chemistry, and physics, and in almost nothing else. At Cal Tech, where he did his graduate work under a leading solid-state physicist, he collaborated with another student in an experiment demonstrating the feasibility of using masers in radio astronomy to detect and amplify certain types of signals. This experiment attracted a good deal of attention, and he was offered assistant professorships at several universities, among them Michigan and Columbia.

Instead of accepting one of these offers, he went to work in a big industrial research laboratory. He had several reasons for taking this step. One was that the job paid better than an assistant professorship. Another reason was that under the terms of his employment he would be free, unlike most scientists in industry, to do pretty much what he wanted to do in the way of research. In addition, he would be able to put all his effort into research. This seemed very important to Cantelli. In his last year at graduate school, and for several months after getting his degree, he had done some teaching, and he had been dismayed at the amount of time it had taken up. "I felt I hadn't really been getting anything done," he told me. "Some of the other instructors would allot themselves a certain amount of time to prepare a class, and refuse to run over their allotment. I was too much of a perfectionist. I couldn't bear going into a class without being fully prepared."

Cantelli had also been dismayed by what he had seen of the life led by junior faculty members. "As an assistant professor at any good university you have a lot of pressures on you," he said. "You have to produce some significant work within a reasonable length of time, or you don't stay. Until you've made a name for yourself, you also have to worry about where your research money is coming from. If I came here, I knew I'd have no responsibility for financing, no red tape." A final and compelling reason for Cantelli's decision was his feeling that masers had been pretty well picked over from a scientific standpoint, and that he would do well to switch to another area of research. The laser had been invented just a year or so before, and the company for which Cantelli now works was eager to sponsor a wide variety of investigations involving lasers, including studies of nonlinear optics. "Advances in technology of this kind always mean new experimental possibilities are opened up," Cantelli says. "The laser was a particularly exciting tool. It put a whole new parameter at your disposal for doing experiments. It was obvious this was going to be a rich, rich field. Now, I'd never done experiments with lasers, and if I really wanted to get into the field I needed to talk to people, to learn the tricks. I knew that here at the laboratory I could just walk down the hall and look at somebody's equipment, or ask him questions. There are not many places in the world where there is so much concentration on lasers as right here."

Cantelli and the other scientists he works with enjoy a degree of freedom that is quite rare in industrial laboratories. "When you come here you get a laboratory—an empty room," Cantelli says. "If you have some experiments in mind, you start buying equipment. Or you may sit in the library for weeks reading and thinking about what experiments you'd like to do. In the three years I've been here, I've published seven or eight papers. But there's no timetable; you publish them when you're ready. Of course, you're in an atmosphere where things are getting done, and if your work is going slowly you feel uncomfortable." Cantelli's employers are willing to invest heavily in research with lasers at least in part because they hope it will pay off in technological advances from which the company will benefit. But Cantelli is under no pressure to direct his work along the lines that seem most likely to lead to such advances. "All I can honestly say about my work is that it's not harming anyone, and that it may even have some kind of marginal utility," Cantelli says. "I would enjoy it if people did discover some practical uses for what I find. But if the thing I most wanted to do in life was to help society, I wouldn't be a scientist. I would go into some kind of social work."

Each year, some people leave the laboratory where Cantelli works to take teaching jobs at major universities. Cantelli has thought of doing this himself, but only if and when he has established a reputation that can be traded in for an associate or a full professorship, and that will assure him of adequate support for his research. One of his reasons for contemplating such a shift is that his company seldom permits a scientist doing basic research to have more than one technician to help him. "That can be sort of rigorous," he says. "If you really get rolling, that can be a problem. You want people who can help you work out your ideas. That's when some people leave for a university, where they can start collecting some graduate students."

In his present job Cantelli is preoccupied with the experiments he is working on to almost the same degree as when he was a graduate student. Many of the ablest people doing research in his particular sector of solid-state physics work at the same laboratory, and he sits with them in seminars, has lunch with them, visits them in their offices, and sees them at their homes and his. "I'm so engaged with what I'm doing that I don't have much to do with people outside this narrow circle," he says. "It's not that I'm uninterested in other people; it's a matter of alienation through circumstances."

Cantelli generally observes company hours—8:45 A.M. to 4:45 P.M.—but he often returns to the laboratory in the evenings, and sometimes he spends Saturdays there. At home he occasionally reads a novel or a biography, and from time to time he has a go at one of the volumes in a set of the Hundred Great Books in which he and his wife invested a couple of years ago. He does most of his reading, however, in magazines such as *Harper's, Common-weal*, and *Scientific American*. He is a Roman Catholic, and attends mass regularly. "At college, I was worried about the lack of connection between the religious and the scientific views of the world," he says. "But I don't worry any more. Every scientist is aware of an order about the universe. I like to think of it as having been imposed by some spiritual being, by God." Cantelli is also untroubled, in any personal sense, by the moral questions that have troubled so many scientists in the years since Hiroshima. They seem to have no relevance to the effects he produces and observes with such pleasure in his laboratory. "Sometimes I think I live in an ivory tower," he told me. "I just don't have these problems."

Most people would agree that *George Carpenter*, an engagingly sardonic man who teaches chemistry at a leading eastern university, has had an enviable career. Twenty-two years ago, when he was just out of graduate school, he helped to solve a problem that had baffled chemists for more than half a century, and by doing so opened the way for a series of notable achievements in the synthesis of organic compounds. Although no single thing that Carpenter has done since then has been quite so spectacular, there are few other organic chemists in America whose work is so widely admired. Young chemists from all over the world compete for the privilege of working in his laboratory for a year or two, and the respect he commands in industry is such that by spending no more than three weeks a year consulting with chemical and pharmaceutical firms he can add $12,000 to $15,000 to the $24,000 a year that he earns by teaching and research. He has been honored by election to the National Academy of Sciences.

Yet when Carpenter speaks of his career, and of the situation in which he finds himself, the strongest impression he conveys is one of disenchantment. It doubtless stems in part from an awareness that at the age of forty-eight he has not accomplished all that he once hoped to do—a form of melancholy to which few men who have passed their fortieth birthdays are altogether immune. But Carpenter's bitterness, one quickly realizes, has as much to do with success as with failure. He is angered and depressed by the price that American scientists have to pay for success, and by the temptations that beset them both before and after the deal is consummated. These feelings are shared to some degree by many scientists, and the circumstances that have given rise to their disillusionment will be examined in detail in later chapters. Here I will simply set down Carpenter's observations on some of the things that trouble him in American science these days:

ON RUNNING A BIG SHOP: "In organic chemistry most of the people who are productive have a lot of students. Technically—in the laboratory—this is a difficult science. One idea may take years to work out. Most of us have lots of ideas. If we didn't work on a number of them, if we just had to work on one at a time, we would dry up. I came to the conclusion that eight to twelve graduate students is about the right number to have in your laboratory, plus four or five postdoctoral people, and maybe two or three undergraduates working on research projects. But sometimes I wonder if I really need such a big establishment. I would like to work in the lab myself sometimes, at least for relaxation. As it is, I just don't have time. But you can't cut down. If I take fewer students, people will think it's because I can't get any more, not because I don't want so many. They'll think I'm losing my grip, and soon the students really will stop coming. There's a man in my department who won't take any government money. He hasn't had a student for years, and so far as I know he hasn't done any research. Anyway, my colleagues would raise hell with me for not bringing in my share of support—'my share' meaning as much as I can get."

ON FINANCING RESEARCH: "A post-doc costs you maybe seven thousand dollars a year, plus three thousand or so for equipment. The university gets some overhead. Then I need money so that I can offer about half my graduate students jobs as research assistants. It all adds up to seventy-five to a hundred thousand dollars a year. I have to get all of this outside. This means proposals to the National Institutes of Health, proposals to the National Science Foundation, proposals to Army Ordnance, proposals to NASA. That's an awful lot of proposal writing. Some people think it would be better if the government gave research money in chunks to universities. The grants would have to carry a proviso that X thousand dollars a year would go to junior faculty members, or they wouldn't get any. Ideally, the rest of the money should be divided up like shares in a whaling voyage, with everyone getting a share based on past performance. The danger is that egalitarianism would take over, and everyone in the department would get the same amount. This evil would outweigh the advantages of not having to do all this damn legwork."

ON THE GRANT SYSTEM: "I served two years on the NSF panel that gives out grants for research in organic chemistry. The proposals from young people were always in fashionable areas where lots of the big men were working. Most of their proposals were for modest extensions of some well-known work. It was depressing. Of course, if they *had* proposed something absolutely new, it would have been rejected out of hand."

ON SCIENTISTS IN INDUSTRY: "For the most part, it's a pretty sorry lot you deal with. I only do consulting because I'm divorced and need the money. To the man just getting out of graduate school, industry looks pretty good. A fresh Ph.D. in organic chemistry can make more than a thousand dollars a month. But you go to a company year after year and you see these youngsters go downhill. Industry destroys them all, without regard to quality. It isn't interested in them as scientists. It turns them into low-level managers. I don't think we can afford to waste scientists this way."

ON THE DIFFICULTY OF REMAINING A SCIENTIST: "You have to struggle like hell to stay in science when you're my age. The rewards for being successful in science in America are poisonous. You are invited to spend six days in Washington on this committee, eight days on that. Besides serving on an NSF panel, I just spent three years as a special adviser on science programs to the president of the university. When I'm working hard at chemistry, I love to talk to people, to go to concerts, that sort of thing. But my mind keeps coming back to chemistry. For years, though, I was worrying about other things. At lunch, I'd find myself talking about how disgraceful it was that NSF was only putting nine million dollars a year into chemistry. When I woke up at five-thirty in the morning, I'd be worrying about what those kooks were doing over in geophysics, or what the university should do about the computer sciences. Someone has to worry about this sort of thing, but why does it have to be a scientist? Why couldn't a bright businessman do most of these jobs for which everyone says you have to have a productive scientist?

"There's an eighty-seven-year-old chemist at Marburg who is still turning out papers that I can't afford not to read. I marvel at this. I have a feeling American scientists are drying up at a relatively tender age. What bothers me is not the people who decide early in their careers that they want to be administrators. The insidious change, the uncontrolled drift, is what worries me. Nobody is standing there to dissuade you from drifting out of science. There's a tremendous burden on each individual to develop his

own protective devices. I've let my secretary go. I often
don't answer my phone. I'm trying to become nastier."

William Aspinwall, a handsome, restless, laughing man
of thirty-nine who is one of the leading astronomers of his
generation, speaks of his life as a scientist in terms that
men have often used in speaking of their search for God.
"When I was young, for many years the world was just like
a fairyland to me," he says. "I thought that what I wanted
to find was the absolute truth, and that science was where
you could find it. Then I began to wonder what truth and
reality were. I thought that in the philosophy of science
you might get to reality through some sudden flash of insight. I read a tremendous amount in the philosophy of
science. At times I passed through great depths of depres-
sion, not believing that I could understand anything at all.
I never did find an answer. I no longer worry about it quite
so much."

If Aspinwall is less tortured than he used to be by his
inability to grasp the nature of the deity he is seeking, it is
because he has concluded that he does not have to do so in
order to be saved. He feels that for salvation it is enough
that he devote himself to gaining deeper insight into the
origin and future of the universe, which is the main goal of
astronomers who, like Aspinwall, study stellar evolution.
He is clear, however, in his belief that the important thing
is the pursuit, not the knowledge that is pursued. He has
asked himself, as other scientists have, what he would do if
someone were to hand him a book containing the answers
to all conceivable questions about the universe. He is convinced that he would not open it. "If it *had* to be opened,
and all the answers were known, I suppose I would try to
go into the church," he says. "I have wanted so badly for
the church to be real. I have wished at times I could be

enveloped in the womb of the church. It would be wonderful. Unfortunately, I'm an atheist."

Aspinwall, unlike most American scientists, usually can give almost all his time to research. Although the observatory with which he is associated has close affiliations with a university, he does no regular teaching and supervises no graduate students. "If you integrate the students into your own research problems, you lose your individuality," he says. "You become something of an administrator. I get a kick out of doing things myself." As Carpenter points out, every successful scientist sooner or later is asked to take a hand in the organization and management of scientific affairs, and when I talked with Aspinwall he had just recently finished three years of intermittent committee work in Washington. It had entailed, among other things, putting in most of a three-month stretch drafting a part of a report dealing with how much money the government should be investing in ground-based astronomy, and what the money should be used for. Although some scientists become addicted to serving on committees, Aspinwall said he had been able to kick the habit without suffering withdrawal pains. "I suppose what committees do is important because it makes it possible for other people to get on with their work," he said tolerantly. He laughed and added, "You know, it's flattering to be asked to serve on committees, to be part of the politics of science. But you've got to organize your life so that you're in a constant state of excitement. I get my greatest kicks out of finding out something new. So I've resigned from all my committees."

Since resigning, Aspinwall has again been free to use his time almost entirely for observing—there are forty-five nights a year when he is assigned the exclusive use of one of the two big telescopes maintained by his observatory— for thinking, for making calculations, and for writing. To simplify his life, and to ward off unwanted interruptions, he has decided, like George Carpenter, to do without a secretary. (He answers his mail, when he answers it at all, by scribbling on the bottoms of his correspondents' letters.) Sometimes he works for sixteen hours at a stretch, and for weeks at a time he may withdraw into a realm he speaks of as the fantasy world of thought. "The only way I accomplish anything is by complete isolation from reality," he says. "I'm speaking of that trancelike state in which ideas appear more real than the trees or the sunshine."

Despite the wonder and ecstasy that he experiences in his work, and the respect he commands among astronomers all over the world, Aspinwall is at times deeply apprehensive. He is haunted by the knowledge that one day his luck and his talent may simply run out. If this were to happen, his life would outwardly show little change. He would presumably go on observing galaxies and stars, collecting prizes, and getting invitations to give lectures and to serve on important committees. But it would be as if he had been abandoned by God after having known what it is to be in a state of grace. Aspinwall can think of nothing more terrible, and it is plain that one reason he drives himself so hard is to assure himself over and over again, through tangible achievement, that the Calvinist God he does not believe in has not deserted him.

III

The Good Professorial Life

THE NOTION that scientific inquiry is the proper business of a university professor is of quite recent origin. Although Galileo taught mathematics at Padua, and Newton at Cambridge, the revolution in scientific thought for which they were so largely responsible had little impact on the curricula of most European universities. Throughout the seventeenth and eighteenth centuries scientific investigations were conducted outside the traditional centers of learning by men who enjoyed the patronage of the rich or who were rich themselves. Robert Boyle was the son of an earl. Lavoisier was a tax collector. Priestley was supported for years by a patron, Lord Shelburne, who employed him as librarian and literary companion, paid him a salary of £250 a year, and furnished him with a house and a laboratory. "By the middle of the [eighteenth] century," J. D. Bernal has written, "no court could be called complete without its Academy of Arts and Sciences in which academicians, usually rather irregularly paid, had to compete for princely favor by producing laudatory odes or amusing experiments."[1]

One of the first institutions to offer scientists an oppor-

tunity to combine teaching with experimentation and research was not a university of the traditional kind, but a
new type of school, the Ecole Polytechnique of Paris. Established in 1794 by the Revolutionary Convention, it was
given the task of strengthening France's industrial and military technology as rapidly as possible. Its distinctive character was derived from its founders' belief that engineering
should be solidly grounded in the physical sciences. "A
new importance was given to the laboratory aspects of
such fields as physics and chemistry. . . . But the innovation which was probably more important though less immediately obvious was the difference in the type of men
engaged in teaching. The students at the Ecole Polytechnique were being taught by men who were the leaders of
their day in research. . . . Never before had the new recruits to science been faced with such a richness of example and attitude from which to learn."[2]

The Ecole Polytechnique not only turned out first-rate
engineers, but was the source of a rich flow of new scientific ideas. Although many older universities, including Oxford and Cambridge, continued for half a century or more
to view science with a certain disdain, the success of the
French experiment had an immediate influence on higher
education on the Continent. Its impact was greatest in
Germany. Technisches Hochschulen, which soon developed close ties with German industry, were established on
the lines of the Ecole Polytechnique for the training of
engineers. At the same time German universities made science academically respectable by offering chairs to leading
scientists and providing them with laboratories in which to
carry out their investigations while simultaneously in-
structing advanced students in the methods of science.[3]

In the United States, science had only a precarious lodg-
ing in colleges and universities until long after the Civil
War. There were exceptions. In 1848, the eminent Swiss

naturalist, Louis Agassiz, quit the service of the King of Prussia to accept the chair of zoology and geology that had been created for him at Harvard by Abbott Lawrence. Joseph Henry conducted some of his most important experiments in electricity while he was professor of natural philosophy at Princeton from 1832 to 1846. But even when, around the middle of the century, Harvard and Yale began to offer special courses of scientific studies, science commanded little respect from either faculty or students. Admission standards for students seeking a degree in science were lower than for those aspiring to a regular Bachelor of Arts degree, and the course of study lasted three years rather than four. At both universities, "the scientific students were considered second-class citizens, too benighted to aspire to the only worthy degree and therefore to be treated with condescension. At Yale, for instance, [scientific] students were not permitted to sit with regular students in chapel." Professors wanting to do scholarly or scientific work generally had to do it on their own time and at their own expense. A physicist named Henry Rowland, surveying the state of American science in 1899, complained that while a good deal of money was being spent on "so-called practical science which ministers to our physical needs," pure science was badly neglected. "We see a few miserable structures here and there," he wrote, "occupied by a few starving professors who are nobly striving to do the best with the feeble means at their disposal."[4]

By 1899, however, American universities were beginning to take scholarship and science seriously. In the past, a typical university in the United States had consisted of a liberal arts college with two or three professional schools— of law, medicine, divinity—attached to it. For advanced work in the arts and sciences one had to go abroad, and each year scores or hundreds of graduates of American colleges sailed for Europe to study at universities there.

Most of them went to Germany, and many were awed and exhilarated by the dedication of German universities to what one American scholar described as the "ardent, methodical, independent search after truth in any and all of its forms, but wholly irrespective of utilitarian applications."[5] Some men returned to the United States determined to establish universities that would be animated by the same spirit. By arguing that the United States could not be counted among the great nations of the world until this was done, they persuaded businessmen to put up the large sums of money that would be required.

In 1876, the first American university to place its main emphasis on research and graduate training, Johns Hopkins, began accepting students. Graduate programs leading to the degree of Doctor of Philosophy were developed at Harvard, Columbia, Yale, Cornell, Michigan, Wisconsin, California, and at other leading private and public universities. When the University of Chicago was established in 1892, President William Rainey Harper announced that faculty promotions would depend more on productivity in research than on the quality of a man's teaching. To be sure, this notion was not at once universally accepted, even by major universities. As late as 1910, the president and trustees of the University of Minnesota took the position, according to one historian of higher education in America, that a chemistry professor's research was "his own private business, much like playing the piano or collecting etchings."[6] But at most universities with any claim to academic distinction this attitude was dead or dying by 1910, and professors were not only encouraged but expected to do scholarly or scientific research.

Although professors are no longer the only people in America who are paid to do scientific research—many more chemists are now to be found doing research in industry than at universities—talented young scientists, as Edward Teller pointed out, almost invariably aim at becoming university professors.[7] Many do so mainly because they are convinced, for reasons that I will discuss a little later, that to have a satisfying career in science they must teach as well as do research.

But universities have other powerful attractions as well. Besides being free to investigate whatever interests him, the academic scientist, once he reaches the rank of associate professor—which he is likely to do when he is still in his early thirties—normally has complete job security. He also has the advantage of being in a community in which administrators wield comparatively little power and tend to be looked down on as men who have shot their bolts as scientists or scholars, or who perhaps never had any bolts to shoot. By contrast, the industrial scientist is enmeshed in a system that confers money and status on people who run things, not on people who think. More often than not, the only way a scientist can gain respect from the managers of the corporation he works for is to become a manager himself. "[The] highly creative individual investigator usually finds that he can live with this state of affairs," two members of the Harvard Business School faculty have written, "because he gets enough satisfaction from the recognition given him by his scientific colleagues outside the company to offset the lack of, or emptiness of, a high level title. It is more difficult for his wife, however, to explain to her bridge table friends why her husband remained a research chemist for twenty years while their husbands have become executives."[8]

Universities also attract young scientists because, so far as basic science is concerned, that is where the action is. Academic scientists contribute roughly two-thirds of the papers published by the principal scientific journals in the United States,[9] and they win an even larger share of the most

coveted scientific honors. Thirty-eight of the forty-three
Americans who won Nobel prizes for science from 1950
through 1966 were university professors, and so are four out
of five American scientists whose "distinguished and con-
tinuing achievements in original research" have gained
them election to the National Academy of Sciences. Professors are also in a large majority on the most important
boards and committees that advise the federal government on scientific matters. In 1967, fourteen of the eighteen members of the President's Science Advisory Committee were men who had spent all or most of their careers on
the faculties of universities. Appointment to a professorship at a leading university is, in sum, rather like being
elected to a good London club with close Establishment
connections.

Quite apart from such worldly considerations, there are
advantages to be gained from close association with other
people who are active in the same field of research. ("The
big fear among physicists," a postdoctoral student told me,
"is somehow getting isolated in some little company and
being given some little problem, where you have no one to
talk to, no intellectually challenging friends.") In the experimental sciences, it may be very important for a scientist to have colleagues to whom he can turn for information about techniques with which he is not familiar, but
which may be useful to him in his own work. Theorists like
to talk with other theorists. "You get a crazy idea and go
chasing to one of your friends and say, 'What about this?' "
a young theoretical physicist explains, "and he'll say 'Crazy,'
and you'll bow your head and go home and think of
another idea. And with the next one your friend may
be interested. . . . There is always a temptation to think
that all ideas you invent by yourself are good by definition.
There has got to be a curb on this, I think. Intercourse at
this level is extremely important." He adds, "The game is,

you try to smash everybody else's theory. Somebody comes up with a theory, and you try to prove it's wrong, and if you can't prove it's wrong, then you start working on it. . . ."[10] An assistant professor of mathematics at M.I.T. told me, "Before I accepted this job I looked into one I had been offered in industry. It was really quite an unusual opportunity. I would have had complete freedom. The main thing that worried me was that I would be isolated. I mentioned this when I was visiting the company, and they said, 'You don't have to worry about that. We have so-and-so and so-and-so and so-and-so coming here regularly as consultants.' I thought, Why not come here to M.I.T., where most of these people would be my colleagues, and where I could sit in seminars with them every week? Besides, the job paid only a thousand dollars more than I am getting here, and it just didn't seem worth it."

It can be argued that this mathematician's decision made good sense even from a purely financial point of view. Although industrial research pays better at the start than an assistant professorship at M.I.T., a scientist who becomes a full professor at M.I.T., or at any one of twenty-five or thirty other universities, can both have and eat his cake. Besides enjoying the autonomy and the other nonpecuniary advantages of an academic career, he is likely to make more money than all but a very few industrial scientists, excluding those who administer research instead of doing it themselves.

For men who entered on scientific careers before World War Two it is hard to think of a scientist as being anything but poor. Only a little more than forty years ago, in a book called *The Natural History of a Savant*, the French physiologist Charles Richet asked: "Why does a young man of twenty say to himself, 'I want to be a savant.' Does he not know that he will never thus attain the joys which luxury affords? His lot, even if he succeeds, will only be a lean living—a bare subsistence. . . . He will have to work in an obscure laboratory. Poor he entered into life: poor he will remain." Richet added, "Nowhere, save perhaps in America, thanks to generous and intelligent millionaires, has society, so-called civilized society, contributed even moderate emolument to the men, young or old, who give themselves up to pure scientific research and so advance civilization."[11]

Even in the United States, the best a scientist could reasonably look forward to forty years ago was genteel poverty. In 1928, the median salary of a full professor at Yale, one of America's richest universities, was only $7,000. According to a study by the American Association of University Professors, this was something less than half of what a man would need to enjoy a standard of living equal to that of a moderately successful New Haven dentist or lawyer. To keep up the appearances demanded by their position, the AAUP reported, Yale professors tended to live in bigger houses than they could really afford, and usually had to take on outside work in order to make ends meet. The AAUP noted that this work tended to be tedious or unpleasant in other ways, often cut deeply into time that might better have been given to productive scholarship, and for the most part paid badly. In a period when few middle-class households were without a full-time servant, the AAUP reported that a Yale professor "with three children of school and college age level must generally maintain the 'mechanic type' of home. The wife does the housework with only partial and occasional hired help . . ."[12]

Genteel poverty is no longer the lot of those Americans "who give themselves up to pure scientific research." Since 1950, academic salaries have more than doubled. Even so, to be sure, there are places like the universities of South Dakota, South Carolina, Missouri, and Oklahoma, where full professors earn an average of less than $11,000 in basic salary and fringe benefits. But figures compiled by the AAUP show that in 1966–67 seventeen major universities– Brandeis, Brown, Cal Tech, Chicago, Columbia, Duke, Harvard, Johns Hopkins, M.I.T., Pennsylvania, Princeton, Rochester, Cornell, Michigan, Stanford, Northwestern, and Yale—were paying full professors an average of at least $19,630. At several of these institutions the average was over $21,000. At more than one hundred other colleges and universities, including Tulane, Iowa State, Ohio State, Purdue, Notre Dame, and the Universities of Indiana, Illinois, Minnesota, Washington (Seattle), Texas, and California, full professors were earning an average of $15,600 to $19,600, in salary and fringe benefits, for a nine-month year.*[13]

Besides their basic salaries, scientists on university faculties very often get extra pay for the research they do. Universities, it is true, try to keep too wide a gap from opening up between the pay of professors who can easily get research grants (scientists), and professors who can't (philosophers, medieval historians, and the like). For this reason, they do not generally permit faculty members to be paid anything above their regular salary for research that they do during the nine months of the academic year. Exceptions to this rule may be made, however, if, for example, the extra pay is for research carried out during time

---

* A Yale philosophy instructor, Norman S. Care, recently described a job interview he had had with a college dean. Care told a Congressional committee, "When he asked me what I thought to be a decent salary for an instructor in philosophy with a completed Ph.D. and I replied with what I considered a reasonable figure ($7,500 to $8,000), he cautioned me 'not to talk like a physicist.'" As this remark suggests, many colleges and universities pay scientists more than they pay humanists. At the universities I have listed, the average compensation of a full professor in any of the natural sciences probably exceeds the university-wide average by several hundred dollars a year.[14]

that a professor might otherwise use for consulting—or, if he happens to be a physician on the faculty of a medical school, time that he might devote to private practice. Sometimes an exception is made because there seems to be no other way to keep a valued professor from moving to another institution (and taking his grants with him). But universities are perfectly happy if a faculty member can arrange for a summer salary, provided the amount he is to be paid does not exceed a specified fraction—usually two-ninths or three-ninths—of his regular academic pay. So much government money is now available for this purpose that it is hard to find a scientist above the rank of assistant professor at any major university who is not drawing a summer salary of several thousand dollars—even if, like Henry Guthrie, he spends his summers in Nova Scotia writing, thinking, and fishing for salmon.[15]

Scientists on university faculties, especially physicists, mathematicians, chemists, and professors of engineering, can also earn a good deal of money as industrial consultants. There are many reasons why business firms retain professors, and not all of them are reputable. A company eager to land a government research-and-development contract may retain a distinguished academic scientist and use him as bait. A company may also retain a professor to pick the brains of his academic colleagues on its behalf; to put his graduate students to work on problems the company is interested in having solved; or to steer the most promising of his students into the company's employ when they leave the university.* As a rule, however, a consultant

* Herbert E. Longenecker, the president of Tulane, has written of a department chairman at an unidentified university who "takes the firm position that if any member of his department wishes to consult with private industry it must be with the company that retains him [the chairman]—at a handsome figure that was arrived at after dickering with a number of competitors who also sought his services." [16]

is hired neither as a spy nor as a procurer. Instead, he may be asked to give his opinion on the feasibility of a new research program a company has in mind; to suggest how a company might go about solving certain technical problems; or to talk with a company's own researchers, evaluate their work, and suggest how its quality might be improved.

Although engineers welcome industrial consulting as a valuable way of keeping up with changing techniques and practices in their fields, most "pure" scientists have little to say for it other than that it pays pretty well. Just *how* well is not easy to determine. Professors who make a lot of money as consultants are often reluctant to talk about it for fear people will think they are neglecting their students and their research, while professors who make only a little are reluctant to talk for fear their colleagues will laugh at them. In 1964, however, some facts on consulting fees were set forth in an article in *Science*, the weekly journal of the American Association for the Advancement of Science.[17] The author, Daniel S. Greenberg, noted that companies pay academic consultants a minimum fee of $100 a day, and went on to suggest that they get away paying so little only because many scientists are naïve. "For example," he wrote, "a young physical scientist was invited to serve as a consultant to the research division of a large industrial firm. The fee, he was told, would be $125 a day. He explained that he would prefer to start at $100 and, if the company found his services satisfactory, the amount could be raised."

Few scientists are quite that naïve. The usual fee paid to a full professor is probably more like $250 a day than $100, and some consultants earn a good deal more. Greenberg mentioned a drug firm that pays its academic consultants annual retainers ranging from $6,000 to $12,000, for which they are expected to attend week-long meetings three times a year with the company's staff. This works out, in the case of the highest-paid of the company's consultants, to $572 a day. A professor identified as "a well-known physical scientist with a specialty that has caused industry to beat a path to his laboratory" told Greenberg that for the last five years he had been devoting one month a year to consulting—most universities do not object to a faculty member's spending an average of one day a week as a consultant—and had earned an average of $50,000 a year in fees. He added that his close contact with industry gave him something more than just money. "It gives me a chance to place my mediocre students," he said. Scientists on university faculties also put in a good deal of time as government consultants, usually as members of advisory panels or committees. The pay for this work is relatively modest, seldom exceeding $100 a day.

There are no statistics that show how much consulting is done by academic scientists, taken as a group, or how many of them do it. Information compiled by the United States Office of Education indicates that in 1961–62 one out of four faculty members at large universities did some consulting, and that they earned an average of $1,900.[18] It is not possible to tell whether scientists did more or less consulting than other faculty members. The Office of Education's figures do suggest, not surprisingly, that full professors earn a lot more money as consultants than their junior colleagues.

To estimate the annual income of a "typical" academic scientist who has reached the rank of full professor, one must therefore make some rather arbitrary assumptions as to how much consulting he does, and how well he is paid for it. Assume that he spends twelve days a year as a government consultant, earning $75 a day, and an additional twelve days consulting with industry at $250 a day. Assume further that he is yearly paid a summer salary equivalent to two-ninths of his academic-year salary. (Three-ninths is a more common arrangement, but there are also some universities that limit summer salaries to two-tenths of the recipient's basic pay.) Then, depending on whether he teaches at a big state university like Indiana or Illinois or California, or at a leading private university, like Princeton or Stanford, his income in 1967, would have been something like this:[19]

	At State University	At Private University
Basic salary plus fringe benefits	$18,300	$21,500
Summer salary	4,100	4,800
Consulting fees	3,900	3,900
Total	$26,300	$30,200

Considering that a professor of physics or chemistry at Harvard or Berkeley or Chicago stands at the top of his profession, this is not exactly big money. A partner in a big Wall Street law firm is likely to be making from fifty to seventy-five thousand dollars a year by the time he is in his forties; a successful surgeon may make more.[20] In 1964, 281 members of the Class of 1954 at the Harvard Business School filled out questionnaires on the occasion of their tenth reunion, and one man out of eight said he already was earning at least $30,000 a year. Two out of three said they expected to be in this bracket by the time their twentieth reunion came around. There are very few professors who can afford to collect paintings or classic cars, live in twenty-room houses, keep riding horses, take winter vacations at Montego Bay or Antigua, or indulge in other luxuries enjoyed by successful stockbrokers and corporation lawyers.

But at the upper levels of academic life there are many thousands of scientists who can afford—or will be able to by the time they reach their forties—luxuries of the kind that are regarded as essentials by most prosperous middle-class Americans.[21] They can buy summer cottages, drink Scotch, build backyard swimming pools, buy their suits at Brooks Brothers, and send their children to private schools. "It's been enormously helpful to be rich, so to speak," I was told by a middle-aged professor of biology. "My father was a professor too. He taught chemistry at a state university, and when he retired in 1948 his salary was only five thousand dollars a year. When I had to have my teeth straightened it nearly broke my family. But in my own professional career I haven't had to worry about money. I don't have to worry if my kids need braces on their teeth."

The new value that has been placed on the services of academic scientists has affected their laboratories even more than their living standards. The austerity and improvisation that characterized scientific work before World War Two exist mainly in the memories of middle-aged and older men. Their disappearance is due in part to the fact that research in fields like oceanography and high-energy physics requires huge machines that cannot be constructed out of odds and ends in the corner of a basement. But even in fields where huge machines are not needed, the conditions of scientific work have been transformed by the generous public patronage that scientists now enjoy.

In biology, for instance, the nature of this transformation has been described in illuminating detail by the well-known biologist Bentley Glass. "In 1940," he writes, "an assistant professor of biology, a fairly typical scientist, had no special funds for his research. An amount not exceeding hundred dollars annually came from the departmental budget and was used for consumable supplies. He had for his use one moderately good compound microscope and one good binocular dissecting microscope. He made all his own media, did his own sterilizing in a Sears Roebuck pressure cooker, kept his own stocks without assistance, and was grateful for some help in washing up the glassware. . . ." Glass then goes on to describe the situation of a professor of biology in 1960: "[He] has charge of two research laboratories, both supported by funds from the federal government. A senior research associate operates one of these laboratories semi-independently, with a research assistant to aid him. Two research assistants work in the other laboratory. In addition, there are two part-time laboratory assistants to wash bottles, keep animals, and prepare media. . . . There are compound microscopes of the best quality; binocular dissecting microscopes for each worker; phase microscopes; photomicrographic equipment; an X-ray machine; a cold room; constant-temperature incubators, refrigerators, and deep-freeze . . . special rooms and equipment for preparing and sterilizing media and washing glassware; animal quarters—in short, everything that is really needed for an experimental program of some size."*[22]

As Glass indicates, Washington is the main source from which these blessings flow. Government support for research at colleges and universities, which hardly existed before 1940, now amounts to more than $2 billion a year. The ease with which university scientists can command

---

* The change has been equally striking in other fields of science. "The typical Ph.D. production shop," Seymour Tilson, associate editor of *International Science and Technology*, has written, "looks, sounds, and even smells like the average, middling-sized corporate research center—no more mustiness and not much dust. . . . Never has there been so much fancy, high-priced, store-bought research equipment around—from electron microscopes to X-ray diffractometers to infrared spectrographs in nearly every chem lab, on up to particle accelerators, for example, or at least easy access to one nearby. . . . The meteorology boys have airplanes and rockets to carry their instruments; the oceanographers soon will have all the ships and the astronomers all the telescopes they desire to sail or peer through. Even the geologists have long since turned in their burros for jeeps with four-wheel drive and, not infrequently, automatic transmissions too. Computers of course are everywhere or else rapidly on the way." [23]

such support has been pointed up by a Brookings Institution study, *The Effects of Federal Programs on Higher Education*. The author of the study, Harold Orlans, asked some three thousand members of university faculties at twenty-four universities if they had had any support from the government for their research during 1960. The universities chosen by Orlans fell into two groups. Group I consisted of twelve universities ("some of international renown and some of more regional standing") that were getting a great deal of government money; Group II consisted of twelve universities that were getting relatively little. In the branches of science covered by Orlans, the percentage of faculty members of all ranks who said they had had federal support was as follows:[24]

Field	Group I Universities	Group II Universities
Preclinical biosciences (i.e., members of medical school faculties)	93%	78%
Physics	89	73
Chemistry	79	65
Biology, Zoology	74	66
Mathematics	53	37

Since Orlans made his survey, government spending to support basic research in academic institutions has more than tripled, and in some fields—notably in biology and zoology—the percentage of faculty members getting government support would doubtless be higher today.*

Much of the money universities get from the govern-

* In the past four years, however, expenditures have been rising at a much slower rate—about 12 percent a year—than in 1958–63, when annual increases averaged about 30 percent. Since there has been no corresponding reduction in the number of new investigators applying for research grants each year, in most fields it is harder for a young assistant professor to get a grant today than it was in, say, 1963.

ment is for applied research. Some also goes into hybrid projects that may be viewed as either basic or applied. Such projects may involve sophisticated techniques, but are not proposed or supported because of any expectation that they will add significantly to scientific understanding. Rather, they are supported in the hope that they will contribute to the achievement of some practical aim. A professor and his students may spend years, for example, making certain measurements that are of no great interest to other scientists, but that are of great importance to engineers trying to design more efficient nuclear reactors.

But a good deal of money is also available for basic research of the classic kind. Anne Roe, the author of a 1952 study of sixty-four eminent American scientists, reinterviewed fifty-two of her subjects in the early 1960's, asking them, among other things, if they had had any difficulty in getting financial support since World War Two. "The unanimous testimony of these men," she reported, "is that they have had . . . all of the funds they have needed for research, and they have been able to do what they personally wanted to do, and have not had to alter their goals in order to secure research funds." One man, a biologist, said, "I think that in the field of biology today any person who has a sensible suggestion about what he wants to work on can get the fiscal support that he needs to do it, and there is no need for any biologist, or at least any semi-respectable biologist, to feel that he is pressured to work on some particular thing because there is money available for it. There is money available for anything." A more cautious but essentially similar verdict is given by Harold Orlans. He writes that "it is probably true to say that the 'best' scientists can generally get support for the work they want to do; the 'average' scientists, for the work the government wants done."[25]

There are other ways besides those mentioned by Glass in which the academic scientist's situation has changed for the better since 1940. For one thing, he has much more time to spend on research. In 1938, the average university professor in the United States spent eight to twelve hours a week teaching classes, and perhaps ten to twenty hours preparing his lectures and reading and grading student papers. By contrast, at Orlans's twelve Group I universities, the average teaching load in the natural sciences was only six hours a week. At three of the universities it was less than five hours, and at one of these it was less than four.[26]

Scientists are also much freer than they were to travel about the country and the world talking with other scientists. J. B. Adams, the director of a big British research laboratory, has spoken of the evolution of a new type of scientist, the Pilgrim Scientist, who "goes around fertilizing research in many laboratories." Addressing a banquet of the American Physical Society in 1964, Adams observed that the Pilgrim Scientist, like the pilgrim of the Middle Ages, "also has his shrines and religious houses to visit, depending on his branch of research. In high-energy nuclear physics, for example, the equivalents of the old religious houses are Berkeley, Brookhaven, CERN [the European Center for Nuclear Research in Geneva], and Dubna." He went on to say, "just as it was customary for the medieval pilgrim to be fed, housed, and looked after by the monasteries, so the modern research laboratory must set aside funds to pay foreign pilgrim scientists and to send its own on tour."[27]

A well-known biologist, who described himself happily as "an overprivileged professor so far as travel is concerned," summed up for me his peregrinations during a recent four-year period. In 1960, he said, he went to Puerto Rico on a mission for the National Science Founda-

tion, to Holland to attend a UNESCO conference, to Kuala
Lumpur (as a guest of the British government), to Java,
and to Australia. The following year he attended a scientific meeting in Moscow, made a scientific pilgrimage to
Delhi via Bukhara and Samarkand, and then went to Nepal
for a month of mountain climbing. In 1962, he traveled to
Australia, via Tahiti, and then to Johannesburg, where he
read a paper at a meeting and then left for a three-week
trip through the South African game preserves. ("Of
course, you have to watch yourself," he said. "Just yester-
day, I was asked to drop everything and come to Uganda
for six weeks. You could spend all your time going to
Uganda.") In 1963–64, he was a visiting professor at Oxford. During the time he was there, he flew back to the
United States four times—his travel expenses were paid by
the National Institute of Health, which sponsors most of
his research—to catch up with what was going on in the
sizable laboratory he heads at his own university. "It was a
deliciously relaxed year," he told me. "I finished one book,
started another, and got all full of culture."

Some traveling by academic scientists is in connection
with consulting jobs. For example, the biologist whose
travels I have just described went to Australia because the
Australian government had asked for his opinion on a new
method of growing rice with which it was experimenting.
Scientists also do a certain amount of pointless junketing.
This may consist of going off to a resort hotel or conference
center to exchange views on "The Megalopolis and Its Dis-
contents" with people in other fields who are also escaping
for a few days from the need to think. Social scientists
generally outnumber natural scientists at such affairs, but
there are well-known men in almost every scientific field
whose natural habitat is the interdisciplinary conference.
"The level of discourse," Jacques Barzun has written, "al-

lows them to wade comfortably across any difficulty, and the atmosphere—to say nothing of the food and drink—is conducive to their mental repose."[28]

But most of the moving about that scientists do is for the purpose of talking with other people in their fields. Derek J. de Solla Price, a historian of science, has pointed out that the most gifted and productive workers in each scientific discipline are usually banded together in an informal association not unlike the so-called Invisible College that was the forerunner, in seventeenth-century England, of the British Royal Society. Members of these latter-day Invisible Colleges, Price writes, maintain "an elaborate apparatus for sending out not merely reprints of publications but preprints and pre-preprints of work in progress and results about to be achieved. . . . In addition to the mailing of preprints, ways and means are being found for physical juxtaposition of the members. They seem to have mastered the art of attracting invitations from centers where they can work along with several members of the group for a short time. This done, they move on to the next center and other members. . . . For each group there exists a sort of commuting circuit of institutions, research centers, and summer schools giving them an opportunity to meet piecemeal, so that over an interval of a few years everybody who is anybody has worked with everybody else in the same category."[29]

Scientists are at their most peripatetic in summer. Many spend their summers working in other laboratories than their own. Each year, for instance, more than two hundred biologists spend their summers doing research at the Marine Biological Laboratory at Woods Hole, on Cape Cod. (Woods Hole is especially popular with wives of biologists who teach at landlocked Midwestern universities.) Many thousands of scientists also go to summer research conferences. These include the Gordon Conferences, which are held annually in New England under the auspices of the American Association for the Advancement of Science. Each conference—there were fifty-four in 1965—runs for a week, and attendance is limited to about a hundred scientists, all of whom must be actively engaged in the study of, for example, low temperature geochemistry or energy coupling mechanisms. Proceedings are off the record, and participants are therefore free to advance new ideas in a tentative way, and to present purely speculative hypotheses without having to worry that what they say may find its way into print and be misinterpreted.[30] There are also so-called summer institutes. These are actually two- to four-week courses for postdoctoral and advanced graduate students, taught by a faculty that is often made up largely of fellow members of the same Invisible College. Physicists have been particularly successful in getting international organizations such as NATO to finance schools of this kind. After spending most of an August afternoon talking with a theoretical physicist in his office at Columbia University, I remarked on the fact that his phone had rung only once. He explained that many of the graduate students in the physics department were at an institute in Norway. "Four or five people are at another institute in Italy," he added. "They all seem to be held at pleasant places. It's almost unheard of now to spend the summer here in New York."

As I have suggested, all scientists who teach at American colleges and universities do not lead the sort of professional life I have been describing. In 1965, Dr. Fay Ajzenberg-Selove, a professor of physics at Haverford, described for a Congressional committee the situation confronting a young physicist who goes into college teaching: "His teaching load will typically involve fourteen or more contact hours per week (only a handful of colleges have teaching loads of nine hours or less), he will generally have inadequate technical and secretarial help, he will be professionally isolated, and his chances of obtaining federal support will be very poor indeed." She added, "A good young Ph.D. physicist who wishes to combine teaching and scholarly work would then appear to be out of his mind if he were to choose a college position . . ."[31]

There are perhaps twenty to twenty-five colleges where faculty members do have productive scientific careers. (Haverford is one of them.) But even at some of the most distinguished liberal arts colleges, a serious commitment to research cannot always be honored, and this in turn is making it harder and harder for them to prepare students adequately for graduate work in the sciences.[32]

A young biologist, *Harold Polk*, told me that in the two years he had been teaching at a famous old college in the Midwest he had been unable to get any research done, and that he was unlikely to get any done in the future unless he could get more laboratory space, and a lighter teaching schedule. "If you ask for these things," he said, "the traditional answer here is, 'No; this is a teaching institution.' But is this realistic? Even at the undergraduate level, you can't entirely separate teaching from research any more. If our seniors are going to be able to compete as graduate students with students from Harvard and Yale and Stanford, they're going to have to have more specialized attention than they are getting here now. I'm talking about their having a chance to learn something about research by working with someone who is deeply engaged in research himself." He added, "I've immersed myself in the students. They're wonderful. And yet if I lose touch with what's going on in biology because I'm no longer really doing any biology myself, I'll be failing them. The good ones will go on to graduate school, and they'll meet, and they'll say,

'Remember old Harold Polk? He wasn't a bad guy. He would have been a pretty damn good teacher if he had kept up with what was happening in his field."

There are universities, as well as many colleges, where scientists have to contend not only with heavy teaching schedules, but with an atmosphere of complacent mediocrity. "They used to lock the departmental library at five o'clock," an organic chemist told me, in recalling his years as an assistant professor at a huge second-rate private university. "There were plenty of chemists to talk to, but in this business there's a critical quality as well as a critical mass. Out there, everybody's idea of a big evening was to take a box supper and spend the evening square dancing."

But while there are many thousands of men and women trained in science who hold academic jobs in which they have little chance of making even a modest contribution to the sum of scientific knowledge, there is now a very large body of academic scientists who have no one to blame but themselves if they are unproductive. Their position has been glowingly portrayed by Gerald Holton, a professor of physics at Harvard and formerly the editor-in-chief of *Daedalus*, the journal of the American Academy of Arts and Sciences. Writing in *Daedalus* in 1962, Holton described a typical American physicist, and said it was clear "that here is a new type of scholar." He went on, "Indeed, he and each of many colleagues like him has available for life the security, means, and freedom to do research that Alfred Nobel hoped to give by his prize to the few outstanding persons in the field. Most significantly, our new scientist is new in that he does not regard himself as especially privileged. The facilities for doing creative work are being accepted and used by him without self-consciousness and with the same naturalness as one accepts the convenience of a telephone."[33]

Even at Harvard scientists do not necessarily lead such serene lives as Holton's portrait might suggest. For most academic scientists, research is only a part-time activity. Although a professor of physics or chemistry at an American university does much less teaching than he would have had to do twenty-five years ago, he still spends half his time preparing lectures, meeting classes, and talking with graduate students. According to a survey made in 1964 by the American Council on Education, he also spends about a fifth of his time—ten hours, say, out of a fifty-hour work week—going to meetings of faculty committees, writing letters to recommend students for jobs or fellowships, working up research budgets, and doing other administrative chores.[34] In a book called *Scientists: Their Psychological World*, Bernice Eiduson suggests that many academic scientists feel themselves the victims of a malign conspiracy aimed at keeping them from doing any research at all. "Some tell of jumping out of bed in the morning," she writes, "joyful in the knowledge that they will soon be doing the work they like the most. They rush to the laboratory and once there, coffee cup in hand, become busy immediately. However, they are soon involved with administrative duties. . . . During the entire day they are confronted with one problem: How can they squeeze a little research time into the mass of activities that have to be cleared away first." She adds, "A few . . . engage in research by establishing an elaborate and ascetic work regime, a regime in which no phone calls are permitted, no personal communications, no interruptions. Frequently, research is even done behind locked doors."[35]

A good many academic scientists look on teaching, apart from presiding over graduate seminars and directing the research of doctoral candidates, as a tiresome chore, and contrive to do as little of it as possible. At Orlans's twelve Group I universities, 18 percent of the scientists who

answered his questionnaire said they had done no undergraduate teaching at all during the 1960–61 academic
year.[36] But as I have said, there are many more academic
scientists, or would-be academic scientists, who consider
teaching a valuable privilege. One reason why this is so
was pointed out some years ago by the late J. Robert Oppenheimer. Oppenheimer observed that "in the relatively
creative field, the fields where imagination is involved, in
fields where you can't have any guaranty of success, it is
nice to be paid for something different from having good
ideas." He added, "It is nice to be able to get up and say, 'I
will teach class today and be a genius tomorrow.' "[37]
Other scientists take a more positive view. Like Henry
Guthrie, the biologist whose career is sketched in Chapter
II, they may find that lecturing has the salutary effect of
making them organize their ideas and observations. "I look
on teaching as a means of forcing myself to inquire out the
interconnections between things," an astrophysicist told
me. "It makes the intellectual juices flow." George Carpenter feels that if he were to stop teaching he would lose the
ability to distinguish between what is significant and what
is trivial in his field of research. "If you want your work to
have any impact at all, you must do something that will
change concepts," he said. "So you try to lead a life that
will force you constantly to judge ideas for their potential
significance. You can't afford to become too highly specialized. In industry, there is no force operating on a scientist
to keep him broad. The corrective for me is the obligation
to teach."

The same point is made by another chemist, Richard
Wolfgang, who teaches at Yale. In a recent article in *Science*, Wolfgang argued that teaching—especially teaching
bright undergraduates—is one of the best ways for a scientist to gauge the importance of his own work. "An outstanding student is probably at least as bright as his in-

structor," Wolfgang wrote, "less informed but also less prejudiced. He asks what the significance of a certain topic may be, needing to see it in its proper perspective, so that it explains to him a significant aspect of the working of nature. A good professor always tries to answer such a question. Usually he succeeds, but sometimes he fails— and is perhaps left wondering if the subject really does matter that much. The net effect is that in the élite student's unencumbered search for truth, he sometimes takes his professor with him. . . . The net effect of this student pressure is to help keep science from turning inward towards sterile cult and fashion."[38]

Young scientists often give more personal and less abstract reasons than these for wanting to teach. "Some of the reasons that impel students to seek out teaching in addition to research," a young biologist wrote me, "are the same ones that impel anyone to teach anything—desire to communicate knowledge, desire to generate new ideas through dialogue, etc. These might be called the 'esthetic' reasons, and are necessary for any sustained interest in creative teaching." He went on to speak of the value of teaching as a means of organizing and evaluating ideas, and then turned to "a third class of reasons that . . . could be called 'dissatisfaction with research.' I think that many students regard teaching as an opportunity for rewarding personal experiences in a profession that is sometimes more competitive than it needs to be," he explained. "I think that the instincts that lead a sensitive researcher to share his knowledge with others, and to test his thinking by dialogue with students, are certainly sharpened by a desire to retreat from the aspects of research as it is presently practiced that are antagonistic to the 'true' spirit of creative investigation—these being primarily publication without thorough investigation, covetousness of experimental data and ideas, and preoccupation with prestige."

But teaching, particularly teaching undergraduates, can be a trap. A young scientist who puts too much time and thought into teaching may be passed over for promotion because he has not been sticking to business—that is, to research. There is nothing new about this. More than twenty-five years ago Logan Wilson observed that in "lesser institutions and on lower levels in leading universities, the teaching function still has a primacy over the research function, yet everywhere there is an attitude among the academic élite that dismisses meticulous attention to instruction as a deflection from the 'higher' purposes of scholarship and science."[39] But an academic scientist who wishes to keep from perishing must publish even more today than he did before World War Two, if only because he must compete for grants and jobs with a growing number of scientists—on postdoctoral fellowships, and in government and industrial laboratories—who can give all or most of their time to research.

A scientist who is spending thirty-five hours a week teaching, preparing to teach, and doing administrative work may be unable to mount the sustained effort that may be required if he is to do anything significant in the way of research. A well-known industrial scientist, Conyers Herring, has pointed out that in academic science "the size of the minor fraction of the week that is left for research is of critical importance: If it is too small, the efficiency with which it can be used in the conduct of research decreases drastically."[40] "Some people can turn from one thing to another," a scientist told Anne Roe. "My problem is to get long stretches of consecutive time so that I can live with my research problem. I can't do this with hit-and-run tactics."[41] This often worries young scientists who have left graduate school feeling confident that they can both teach and do good research. After eight months as a postdoctoral fellow at a private research institute, the young biologist whom I have quoted earlier in this chapter wrote me, "I am still anxious to try to teach. However, I look at it more apprehensively now. As I go more deeply into research (i.e., work more independently) I find that it requires more and more attention and concentration. . . . I am more apprehensive about trying to combine research and teaching, for fear that I will have to compromise both." He went on to speak of a friend who had been teaching mathematics at Cal Tech for the past two years: "I think Joe has found something of the same thing with teaching. He works conscientiously at preparing his lectures, and finds that he spends more and more time rewriting, polishing, revising—trying to make them perfect."

Furthermore, young scientists who think they would like to teach undergraduates sometimes find the actual experience disappointing. Teaching twenty or thirty juniors and seniors is one thing, but lecturing to several hundred freshmen and sophomores, many of whom are interested only in getting through the course with as little sweat as possible, is another. A scientist who teaches such a course, and is eager for the stimulating contact with undergraduates that he might enjoy at Swarthmore or Oberlin or Reed, can of course make himself available to students outside of the lecture room. But he is likely to find that for every student who comes to his office to ask searching questions, there are half a dozen who come to complain about their grades.

Then, too, a scientist at a university is seldom free to teach undergraduates what he thinks they should learn, in the way he thinks they can best learn it. As a rule, he has to teach what somebody else has been teaching for the past ten years, or what a faculty committee has decided should be taught. It is much easier for a scientist to be daring and imaginative in his laboratory than in a classroom. As Christopher Jencks, a student of academic organization and folkways, has written, "The faculty can collectively do away with grades, substitute papers for examinations, substitute tutorials or small seminars for lectures, or reorganize the course system so that students study subjects sequentially rather than simultaneously. But an individual professor who wants to make such changes in his teaching can do so only with the greatest difficulty, after months or years of politicking and endless committee meetings." Jencks notes that "on virtually every major university campus in America there are professors who want to develop an interdisciplinary science program for nonscientists, start a small residential college where undergraduates will have a chance to get to know a small group of faculty, or whatever. These ideas rarely get off the ground. . . . Even if an idea is accepted in principle, departments are not willing to release 'their' members from conventional teaching duties to try something different."*[42] When a scientist does manage to push through a major curricular reform, success must be its own reward. No one gets elected to the National Academy of Sciences, or is invited to travel around the world, because he has reorganized the freshman physics course at Cal Tech or Wisconsin.

At the beginning of his career an academic scientist has few administrative duties. But the load quickly piles up, and by the time he is in his forties and a full professor he is likely to be spending as much of his time on administration

---

* In the opinion of some members of its faculty, one of the advantages of teaching at the University of California's new San Diego branch, which is to consist of twelve relatively small, semiautonomous colleges, or miniature universities, is that they can experiment with new ways of organizing undergraduate instruction. A biologist who had been head of his department at a leading private university told me that he was going to San Diego partly because he had definite ideas about the way students should be introduced to the biological sciences, and he saw a chance to put them into effect there.

as he is teaching undergraduates. Professors who are chairmen of their departments are even more heavily burdened. The American Council on Education's survey indicated that chairmen of university physics departments spend, on the average, 47 percent of their time on administration, 32 percent on teaching, 14 percent on research and writing, and 7 percent on professional activities such as consulting, going to conferences, and giving lectures outside the university.[43]

It is often assumed that the academic scientist's appetite for government grants, and his dependence on them, are the main reasons why he puts so much time into administration. Certainly he spends a lot more time at it than he did thirty or forty years ago. In the early 1930's, scientists on the faculty of the University of Chicago were giving an average of two and a half hours a week to administration, or only about a third as much time as scientists at Orlans's Group I universities were giving to it in 1960–61. But government patronage does not appear to be the main reason for the change. If it were, one would expect to find philosophers and English professors doing less administrative work than physicists and chemists. But according to the American Council on Education, the opposite is more likely to be true. The average young English scholar, the Council's survey showed, spends 15 percent of his time on administration, and the average senior scholar 21 percent. In physics, the corresponding figures are 8 percent and 20 percent.[44]

These figures show the enormous amount of time that members of university faculties, scientists and nonscientists alike, devote to the management of academic affairs. Much of this time is spent serving on faculty committees— doing such things as weighing the merits of making all graduate students do some teaching and deciding how parking space is to be allocated. There are departmental as well as faculty committees; a department with twenty-five or thirty members may have up to a dozen regular committees and an equal number of subcommittees. Because the addition of a new member may affect not only the prestige of a department, but the balance of power within it, hundreds or even thousands of faculty man-hours may be devoted to the filling of a single vacancy. "The average salary of an assistant professor is approximately that of a bakery truck driver," Caplow and McGee point out in *The Academic Marketplace*, "and his occupancy of a job is likely to be less permanent. Yet it may require a large part of the time of twenty highly-skilled men for a full year to hire him." A professor whom they interviewed described the process as follows: "We had discussed the problem many times in staff meeting. We did a great deal of thinking on this. Our first step was to bring together a committee. They met a number of times trying to decide the qualities to be looked for and then to dig up suitable people to fill the role. After a number of meetings it was boiled down to five men. One man notified us he couldn't be considered. The other four were brought here at intervals of a week or two. They met with each member of the staff and discussed their specialty. Lastly we invited each to give a paper. We brought in heads of other departments and members of the administration to hear them. They added their impressions to our own. We quickly centered on two men. It was difficult to decide; they had highly contrasting interests, abilities, and accomplishments. There were two or three staff meetings before the vote. The needs of the department were examined. We asked ourselves, 'Do we need glamour or promise?' " The professor went on to say, "The four men who came each spent about half a week with us. The committee had got out an elegant and complete biography on each man prior to his visit. The vote was taken the week following the appearance of the last man. The Chairman saw the Dean the day afterward, and the Dean said, 'Go to it,' so the letter was sent that day. . . . The vote included the assistant professors, since it was made at that level."[45]

Most academic scientists look on administrative and committee work as a disagreeable necessity, like the income tax. A few manage to avoid it by a calculated display of inefficiency, or by agreeably consenting to serve on committees and then forgetting to show up at meetings. Others resign themselves as cheerfully as they can to doing more than their share. A biologist serving a three-year term as chairman of his department at a state university says, "I've been training graduate students for twenty years. I know exactly what I'd be able to contribute to research if I didn't take this job. The contribution I could make to the university in science would not justify my turning down this administrative position. I'm not personally ambitious . . . to be a university administrator. At the end of the third year, I will take a leave and get refurbished and pick up my research again."[46] Sometimes resignation is deeply tinged with bitterness. A physicist in his late thirties, who had been for several years the associate director of a research laboratory affiliated with a big eastern university, told me he had taken the job because someone had to do it, and because he was better qualified than anyone else on the staff. "I have lots of friends who don't undertake responsibilities—or who don't take seriously the responsibilities they do assume," he said. "I don't criticize the people who won't have anything to do with administration. Money goes into them, and physics comes out. But my taking on the job of administering the scientific end of things here has enabled other people to do more work than I have been able to do."

The reluctance of scientists to become part-time administrators is due in part to a realization that administration is less compatible with research than teaching is. "I couldn't do an administrative job and do research too, because to me research is always a one-hundred percent job," a scientist told Anne Roe. "You've got to live it all the time. . . . Teaching isn't so bad because you can, if you're fortunate, always teach them something related to your research, so you can tie the two together. In fact, I think it's a good distraction because you can't for too long get in the routine of nothing but research."[47]

To give up research entirely in favor of administration has traditionally been regarded by scientists as a confession of scientific impotence, or as the act of a man who has been seduced from the true way of science by the lure of money and power. As Bernice Eiduson writes, "there is an implicit notion that there is a 'real' scientist or a man who is doing the 'real' scientific duty, the hard, back-breaking work of science, putting in the effort where in the long run it most pays off: at the laboratory bench. It is this man who is the real intellectual, whose work is tied up with the main goals of science. . . . Other functions are of lesser value; therefore the scientists who perform them are weaker and are less 'real scientists.' "[48]

Many first-rate scientists nevertheless wind up their careers as deans, or provosts, or permanent department heads, or directors of research institutes, or civil servants who help distribute grants to their former colleagues. In 1948, when Anne Roe began work on *The Making of a Scientist*, only a few of her sixty-four subjects were deeply involved in administration. Fifteen years later, however, when she interviewed most of them again, eleven of the eighteen biologists with whom she talked, and sixteen of the nineteen physicists, held administrative jobs, or had held them at the time they had retired. Ten were heads of universities, museums, or other institutions; nine were department chairmen; five were directors of laboratories; two were deans; and one was an industrial research manager.[49]

As a rule money has little to do these days with this evolution. Although university presidents and deans make somewhat more money than most professors, the difference is less than it was twenty-five years ago, and few academic scientists take administrative jobs primarily because they want to live better. More often, the scientist who becomes an administrator simply surrenders to circumstances. The surrender is seldom sudden, and may extend over many years. It may begin when a man is in his late thirties and is asked to sit in for his department chairman for a year while the chairman is away on sabbatical leave. He complains, sometimes bitterly, sometimes humorously, about how much of his time is taken up with answering mail, scraping up money for colleagues who feel they have been short-changed by Washington, and worrying about who is to teach Professor X's course while Professor X is on leave and his substitute, Professor Y, is spending a month in Geneva on an urgent government mission. But he finds, to his surprise, that he does this sort of thing fairly well, and that it has its rewards. He realizes that it is only at long intervals that the researcher enjoys the feeling (or illusion) of solid accomplishment that the administrator can enjoy merely by emptying his in-box.

At the end of his year, the temporary chairman is genuinely glad to revert to the professorial ranks. But his talent for keeping his desk clear and his success in keeping people in his department reasonably happy have been noticed. Three years later, when the head of his department leaves for another university, he is offered the chairmanship on a permanent basis. He turns it down, protesting to the president of the university with a bit more vehemence than the situation really demands that he is a research man, not a goddam executive—a point that he emphasizes by neglecting to have his hair cut, and by showing up for the inter-

view in a tweed jacket that looks as if it is made of moldy
burlap and trousers that he would normally wear only
when cleaning out his cellar. But his conscience bothers
him a little—*somebody* has to run things—and a few months
later he accepts an invitation to serve on a committee that is
charged with advising the government about what it should
be doing in oceanography. He rather enjoys wrangling with
his fellow committeemen, and discovers that he has a
modest gift for engineering durable compromises. He also
discovers that he likes sitting around a table with sub-
cabinet officers and high-ranking military and scientific advisers and talking about the politics of scientific patronage—
a form of gossip whose pleasure is enhanced by the virtuous
conviction that it is gossip in a good cause.

Four years later, when he is nearing his fiftieth birthday,
he is once again offered the department chairmanship.
This time he accepts. He continues to teach and to do some
research. But while he is complaining about how little time
he has to spend in the laboratory, and explaining that he
has taken on the chairmanship only until someone with a
real bent for administration can be brought in, he realizes
that research is losing some of its old fascination. This is
not to suggest that scientists are necessarily washed up
before they are fifty. Oswald Avery was sixty-six when he
and two young colleagues at the Rockefeller Institute
opened the way for a new and deeper understanding of
heredity by their classic demonstration, in 1944, that DNA
is the chemical substance responsible for the transmission
of genetic characteristics. Some scientists remain productive well beyond the age at which most Americans retire. A
study of eminent nineteenth-century scientists has shown
that those who lived to the age of eighty or more published
nearly two-thirds as many scientific papers when they
were in their seventies as they had in their thirties.[50] But
more often than not, scientists do their important work in

their twenties and thirties, before they become inhibited
by knowing too many reasons why a new theory or conjec-
ture that challenges prevailing beliefs is likely to be wrong.

In any case, the new department chairman finds as time
passes that he can contemplate with only mild dismay the
idea of giving up research altogether. His equanimity is
bolstered by the revelation, which comes to him while he
is serving a term as chairman of his university's division
of natural sciences, that it can be quite satisfying to hack
one's way through the undergrowth of custom and prerog-
ative, and open up new clearings in the academic jungle.
When the job of dean of the faculty is offered to him he
takes it, without bothering to proclaim that he is only taking a temporary leave from his true vocation. "There's a lot
of snobbishness and hypocrisy about administration," one
of Anne Roe's subjects remarked. "I have listened to some
of my colleagues from time to time through the years talk
about the importance of research and scientific work and
that everything else is sort of sordid materialism. Many of
these people will go on through their lives producing pedestrian papers on matters that are really of no importance
and glorifying this as the research enterprise. If you go
into administration you must believe that this is a creative
activity in itself. . . . The problems in a position like mine
are almost unbelievable in their diversity and importance.
This is part of the excitement of it. In both research and
administration the excitement and the elation is in the
creative power. It's bringing things to pass. Perhaps it's
more action than simple knowledge, but it has a reward
too. Now I think this is more exciting than research."[51]

Scientists are perhaps more tolerant of administrators
than they used to be. As they become more dependent on
machines and money, their scorn is often tempered by
gratitude—gratitude for the department head who relieves

them of tiresome paper work in their dealings with the
government, gratitude for the laboratory director who is a
good money raiser, gratitude for the government program
officer who understands what the scientists he deals with
are trying to do, but who does not try to substitute his
scientific judgment for theirs.

Some scientists argue that administration is now much
too important to be left to men who take it up because
they are not making out very well as scientists, or because
they are tired of doing research. They feel that able scientists should sometimes be encouraged to go into administration early in their careers. A biologist who is noted both
for his scientific and his entrepreneurial talents told me
approvingly that one very able student of his had quit academic life while he was in his thirties, and was now running a big government research laboratory. "After Ted had
gotten his degree here and had been teaching at a university for a few years," he said, "he went to Washington to
spend a year evaluating research proposals in his field for
one of the government agencies. While he was there he
found he could talk Texan with Senators and Congressmen
—he came from Texas—and he never went back to teaching. He has a sort of guilt feeling about this, but I think he
is quite justified on social grounds. Most of my colleagues
here feel the same way. We recognize the value of the
government's having scientifically-trained managers. Some
scientists just have to give up scientific careers to become
managers. Myself, I don't get my kicks spending half my
time being a psychiatrist for members of the department
and the other half of my time talking to philanthropoids.
But my attitude is that somebody has to be a dean, so let's
have a good one, and let's not sneer at him."

Even in this statement, however, one senses a conviction
that although it may be better to be a good dean than a
mediocre scientist, the best thing of all is to be a really

good scientist. It is hard to imagine a scientist urging a student whom he considers brilliant to throw over science for an administrative career. While the scientist who becomes a university president or the head of a research institute may find more room for the exercise of his particular talents than he had as a researcher, he is usually aware that no matter what political or organizational miracles he may bring to pass, they are unlikely to yield moments of the kind of which the physicist I. I. Rabi has spoken. "Although scientists don't write about these moments of exultation and ecstasy so different from the everyday routine of research, these fleeting visions can in one flash reward one for years of patient and exhausting work," Rabi told a Washington audience in 1963. "At these times the scientist is filled with profound awe and humility that such wonders should be revealed through him. There is a quality about science, or rather about nature, which is always miraculous in its originality. To obtain a glimpse of this wonder can be a reward of a lifetime."[52] The administrator may, of course, comfort himself with the reflection that he is doing more for science and his fellow men than he would be able to do as a researcher. But inasmuch as scientific immortality, as well as the joys of which Rabi was speaking, are reserved for men who discover things and not for men who run institutes, this can be a somewhat melancholy thought.

IV

The Price of Affluence

ACADEMIC SCIENTISTS in America have had to pay something for the privileges they now take for granted, and some are inclined to think the price has been too high. "I pine for the day when science was small, and you could do your work without selling your soul for money," William Aspinwall, the astronomer whose career I have sketched in Chapter II, has said. A biologist in his middle twenties wrote me that in his field the competition for jobs and for grants is so fierce that it is "difficult for a person to feel that he can relax and pursue a research problem at his own pace, free to make mistakes and to try imaginative approaches, without anxiety about the periods when his work seems fruitless and his imagination barren." He added, "Research shouldn't be competitive really—the impetus should come from your desire to solve a problem, and the anxiety generated by trying to force solutions only makes the solution more difficult." A well-known American physicist, Merle A. Tuve, has argued that "the university is no place for a scholar in science today." A professor's life, he told a symposium at the Rockefeller Institute in 1959, has become "a rat race of busyness and activity, managing contracts and projects, guiding teams of assistants, and bossing crews of technicians, plus the distractions of numerous trips and committees for government agencies, necessary to keep the whole frenetic business from collapse."[1]

Observations such as these need not be taken entirely at face value. A great many American scientists—including Aspinwall—manage to do what they want without selling their souls for money. And it is doubtful if there ever was a time when a scientist could accept without anxiety a period "when his work seems fruitless and his imagination barren." ("In science, self-satisfaction is death . . ." Jacques Monod, a French molecular biologist and Nobel laureate, has said. "Unquietness, anxiety, dissatisfaction, and torment, those are what nourish science. Without fundamental anxiety, there is no fundamental research."[2]) Furthermore, complaints about the professorial rat race are sometimes strongly colored by nostalgia. To quote Don K. Price, a political scientist who has studied the changing role of scientists in American political life, some scientists "tend to look back on prewar science as the Reformers looked back to the Primitive Church: a period of austere purity, an era in which no vows were needed to guarantee the poverty of the professor, no scientist was seduced by a government contract, and teaching fellows were obedient." Price goes on to say, "One may well be a little skeptical about this point of view, and suspect that poverty probably brought its distractions no less troublesome than those of riches."[3]

But the fact remains that the rising cost of research, and the nature of the patronage system to which men like Gerald Holton's contented physicist owe their prosperity and independence, have drastically changed—and not entirely for the better—the terms on which success is courted and won in American science. The most significant change is that the academic scientist, in order to succeed, must periodically convince the government or some other patron that an investment of tens or hundreds of thousands of dollars in his particular line of research is likely to yield a higher return, in the form of scientific papers, than an equal sum invested in some other scientific undertaking. He is therefore forced to be a part-time businessman and promoter.

The most conspicuous symbol of the new order is the academic entrepreneur, who is adept at thinking up big and expensive research projects and at persuading the government to pay for them. The entrepreneur may be a man of minimal scientific attainments, but often he is a first-rate scientist who also happens to be endowed with the kind of energy, competitiveness, and organizational skill that one is likely to encounter in, say, a successful manufacturer of electronic devices. Usually he has a keen sense of when the winds of scientific fashion are about to shift, and where they will be blowing next. He knows the right people at the right agencies. He has an impressive air of efficiency and managerial competence, and is likely to use terms like "megabuck" and to speak of administrative chores as "burning up the paper on my desk."

The entrepreneur is often cited by academic administrators as a horrible example of what happens when the government allots research funds to individual professors, and thereby permits them to thumb their noses with impunity at department heads and deans. Not long ago, for instance, the chairman of the biology department at Western Reserve University, Howard A. Schneiderman, undertook to explain to a Congressional committee why entrepreneurs are a menace. Asking the committee to "consider a distinguished scientist in a particular field who may command research support . . . of several hundred thousands of dollars per year," Schneiderman said, "As an individual, he may command more support than the rest of his department, taken all together—more than the chairman of his department and, in some cases, even more than the dean of his college. He is in a position to exercise immense leverage because of the funds at his disposal. In many cases he provides funds for most of his own salary. All of his equipment comes from federal funds, as does the support for six or seven graduate students in the department. He gets his own way and teaches very little. If complaints are made about his activities, he threatens to 'pick up his marbles' and go elsewhere." Schneiderman then explained how an entrepreneur may apply his leverage: "He may indicate a willingness to provide salaries for two assistant professors on his grant, if they can be in areas of interest close to him. This is acceded to by the dean because he has no other source of funds for their salaries, and he wishes to keep our prima donna happy. . . . The Chairman's plans for a balanced department and development are sacrificed to expediency, and new assistant professors are hired who are not part of the department, but become part of the subdepartment operated by one faculty member."*⁴

What bothers critics like Tuve is not so much that the climate of academic science is so congenial to entrepreneurs. They are more worried by the fact that the great majority of academic scientists who have no desire at all to be entrepreneurs nevertheless may be forced to become deeply involved in the business of grant-getting. Few universities have much free money of their own to spend on research, and they tend to use what they have to maintain basic laboratory facilities, to support research in fields where little government money is available, and to tide new faculty members over the period when they are waiting for their first government grants to come through. Even

---

* Academic entrepreneurs are not necessarily as bad as Schneiderman's description might suggest. In the case he sets forth, one can imagine his prima donna contending plausibly that it is a good idea for a small department to be really strong in at least one field, and that the chairman's plans for a balanced department would result only in balanced mediocrity.

at the richest universities, a scientist who wants a summer salary, the services of a technician, or special equipment of any kind must either attach himself to a colleague who can raise the money, or raise it himself. In almost all cases this means applying to the federal government.

Moreover, in applying for a government grant, faculty members are often under strong pressure to ask for more money than they need for their own research.* Professors are commonly expected to help finance the education of graduate students by working up projects on which they can employ students (at government expense) as research assistants. They may be expected to raise money for other purposes as well. A few years ago, the All-University Faculty Conference at the University of California complained that "the heavy expenses of . . . [research by graduate students] are being borne increasingly in many departments by extramural grants. To put the matter bluntly, the individual faculty member, rather than the University, provides the money needed for the supplies and equipment used by his students."[5]

Actually, while deans and department heads may deplore faculty entrepreneurs in principle, they dote on them in practice. In a letter to the same Congressional committee that had solicited Schneiderman's views, a professor of physics at a midwestern university noted that "the very administrators who complain about the divided loyalties of the faculty are the first to urge the professor to work in areas which will bring in money."[6] As Harold Orlans points out, one of the best ways to get on in academic life is to be good at getting grants. Orlans asked scientists on

---

* Some basic research that is done by faculty members under government sponsorship, and most applied research, is financed by contracts rather than grants. However, insofar as basic research is concerned, contracts usually give an investigator the same freedom he would have under a grant, and for the sake of simplicity I have used the term "grant" for both kinds of support.

the faculties of twenty-four universities to consider the hypothetical case of two professors having equal ability as teachers and researchers, but differing from one another in that one, *Alpha*, "has obtained a number of grants and contracts for his research work, including funds for the support of student assistants and the purchase of special equipment," while the other, *Beta*, is getting no outside research funds at all. Which one, he asked, was likely to be promoted faster, to earn a bigger salary, and generally to stand in better with the administration? More than 70 percent of the scientists who answered said *Alpha* would be favored.[7]

The academic scientist's dependence on government patronage has had a tendency, among other disturbing side effects, to debase his motives for writing scientific papers. Articles in scientific journals have come to serve not only to communicate new ideas and observations, but also as a form of currency with which a scientist purchases the privilege of being able to keep on with his research.

It is easy to see how this has come about. A government agency that is supporting basic research naturally wants to be able to show that it is giving its money away wisely. When a grantee writes a paper that is accepted by a scientific journal, this means that in the editor's judgment— usually based on the opinions of two or three respected scientists in the author's field who have been asked to review or "referee" the paper—the author has something to report that deserves the attention of other scientists. Articles in scientific journals, of course, are not all of equal merit. But officials of the Budget Bureau and members of Congressional committees to which agency heads must justify their outlays for basic research do not read scientific papers, and even if they did they would have no way of telling the good ones from the bad. Anyone can count, however, and an administrator feels most secure when he can show that the scientists who get grants from his particular agency produce more papers, or produce them at a lower cost per unit, than the grantees of other agencies.

As a consequence, success in academic science may depend on the number of papers a man writes more than on their quality. This is especially true in the early years of a scientist's career, and many young scientists feel compelled to turn out hackwork even though they would rather address themselves to questions of genuine scientific importance. Seeking answers to such questions is at best a risky business, and success is largely a matter of luck. Lawrence Kubie, a psychiatrist who has had a long-standing interest in the special stresses to which scientists are subjected, has suggested that this is one reason why scientists are, in his opinion, particularly susceptible to certain kinds of neuroses. "As in prospecting for gold," Kubie has written, "a scientist may dig with skill, courage, energy, and intelligence just a few feet away from a rich vein—but always unsuccessfully. Consequently in scientific research the rewards for industry, perseverance, imagination and intelligence are highly uncertain. Success or failure . . . may be almost accidental, with chance a major factor in determining not *what* is discovered, but when and by whom."[8]

A serious failure, however heroic, may be more than psychologically harmful to a young scientist. It may also be disastrous from a practical standpoint. Even if his senior colleagues are inclined to attribute his failure to bad luck rather than bad judgment, a young scientist who fails to publish will find it very hard to get grants for further research, and universities generally take the position that a young faculty member must not only do research, but must pay his own way. "You have to publish, and you have to publish at a certain rate," a young chemist told me. "You have to bet on sure horses, even though that means you

don't grow and develop as much as you might. You pass up
the most challenging line because it would be too risky to
follow. Being a glorious failure at thirty is maybe not so
good as being a moderate success."[9] He went on to speak
of a former colleague. "Charlie spent three years working
on a really hard problem that didn't pan out," he said. "The
poor bastard had to go to work for Du Pont."

Newton and Leibnitz fought bitterly over their respective claims to be recognized as the inventor of the calculus,
and disputes about priority, as Robert K. Merton has
pointed out, "far from being a rare exception in science,
have long been frequent, harsh and ugly."[10] But science
is more competitive today than it ever was before. This is
partly because there are so many more competitors; since
1930, membership in the American Association for the Advancement of Science has risen from 19,000 to more than
110,000. Competition has also been sharpened, however,
by the fact that money is now at stake as well as fame. A
scientist who spends a year or two solving a problem, and
then finds that someone else has solved it just ahead of
him, stands to lose more than a chance at scientific immortality. Like the scientist who spends too much time following a trail that leads nowhere, he runs the risk of losing a
promotion, a grant, or even his job.

A scientist may try to minimize this danger by claiming
a particular area of research as his private preserve. He
may refuse, for instance, to let other scientists work with
certain bacterial strains he has isolated in his laboratory. It
has become more common, too, for scientists to be as secre-
tive as dress designers. "There's a lot of baloney about free
communication and sharing and that sort of thing," a
molecular biologist told me. "But just listen to two men
who run into one another at a meeting or conference. One
says, 'Charley, what are you up to these days?' Charley

says, 'Oh, nothing much.' Knowing smiles from bystanders, who know what Charley is really up to. Afterward you say to Charley, 'Why didn't you tell Bill what you're on to?' He says, 'Oh, well, after all, we aren't absolutely sure, and we wouldn't want Bill going off on a false scent.' What he's really afraid of, of course, is that Bill will rush back to his own laboratory and beat him to the goal line."

In *Scientists: Their Psychological World*, Bernice Eiduson quotes a scientist as pointing out that "there's a lot in being a creative scientist today that hinges on being able to frame a problem, or develop a deal in research, and going out and enlisting support for it."[11] This is certainly true in fields like radio astronomy, oceanography, and high-energy physics, in which data can be collected only with the aid of huge and expensive machinery. The physicist who hopes to persuade the government to give his university several million dollars with which to build a bubble chamber, or who would like to have a satellite placed in a particular orbit to gather certain data in which he is interested, must necessarily give a lot of time and thought to ways and means. James Van Allen has explained what a scientist in this situation may have to do. When Van Allen was asked a few years ago how he got the people in charge of launching space vehicles to let him put his instruments aboard, he replied, "Like other forms of politics, it's a mixture of demonstrated competence, good ideas, and knowing the people in charge. You just can't shovel in written proposals; you have to know the people." He went on to say, "If I didn't know anybody I couldn't get anything done. In this game it's even a real enterprise just to keep up with the flight opportunities. People don't usually come around and tell you things. You have to find out. You have to find out at committee meetings, scientific meetings, and by talking in hallways."[12]

Scientists who do not need expensive equipment may also have to work hard to get support. This may be because their ideas and qualifications do not impress the scientific panels employed by government agencies to evaluate applications for grants in aid of basic research. In such cases, the only way to get support may be to spend a lot of time working up research proposals tailored to fit the needs of agencies that have money to invest in so-called mission-related research on the borderline between basic and applied science. Even scientists of unquestioned ability may have to scrounge for money if they are in a field in which relatively little government support is available. In chemistry, which for many years has been on much shorter financial rations than physics and the biological sciences, a professor may have to piece together support for himself and his students from three or four different sources.

But by and large, scientists at major universities do not have to put an inordinate amount of effort into the business of applying for and administering research grants. When scientists on the faculty of the University of California at Berkeley were asked in 1962 to indicate on a questionnaire how easy or hard it was for them to get grants, only 10 percent said they usually found it either fairly difficult or very difficult. Forty-nine percent said they usually got grants with no difficulty at all.[13] And while a professor who is supporting the work of ten or twelve other people may have a good deal of paper work to do in connection with his grants, the average grantee has little. Neither the National Institutes of Health nor the National Science Foundation, which make more grants to university scientists for basic research than all other government agencies combined, demand very much in the way of progress reports. A grant from NIH or NSF ordinarily runs for two or three years, and may run as long as seven. During this period a grantee may have to do little

more by way of accounting for his progress than to write a
letter once a year summarizing very briefly the work he
and his associates have been doing, and listing any papers
they may have published. When his grant is about to ex-
pire, he will have to spend some time working up a budget
for the next two or three years, and describing in a general
way some of the things he hopes to do in this time. But in
the case of a typical grantee—a neurophysiologist, let us
say, who has been getting $40,000 a year to cover his sum-
mer salary; the salaries of a postdoctoral research associate, a graduate research assistant, and a technician; and
the cost of experimental animals and some simple electronic gear—the job should take three or four days at most.

The price that scientists pay for federal patronage also
includes the time they spend helping to dispense it. More
than two thousand scientists, most of them from universities, are members of panels that evaluate research proposals for the government. Service on one of these panels
may take from three to six weeks a year of a panelist's time.
For example, the advisory councils of the National Institutes of Health, which review the recommendations of
other advisory groups called study sections, usually meet
four times a year, for three days at a time. A former member of the National Advisory Cancer Council writes that
"the paper material sent to each member . . . forms a pile
which is literally from fifteen to twenty inches high per
meeting." He adds, "To give conscientious attention to this
material requires roughly a week of work preliminary to
each meeting."[14]

Being on a panel has its compensations, however. It
marks a scientist's arrival in the scientific world. It permits
him to taste the delights of power without having to take
on the petty administrative responsibilities that go with
being, say, a department chairman. It gives him, as a Presidential committee has noted in discussing the work of NIH

study sections, "personal access to the most advanced of current research and to the scientists involved."[15]

Such access can have great practical advantages. When a promising new area of investigation is opened up, the panelist is in a good position to jump in ahead of the crowd. He can also tip off his departmental colleagues to new developments in their special fields of interest. In addition, from his vantage point as a panelist he may be able to spot young scientists whose talents would be likely to add luster to his department, and whose price in the academic market is still relatively low.

For these reasons, a scientist who is serving on a review panel may be excused from serving on faculty committees and certain other chores. In such cases, part of the time that he gives to the evaluation of research proposals is time that he would otherwise be spending not on research, but on administrative tasks. Moreover, when scientists complain about the work they do as members of review panels, it is legitimate—though impolite—to point out that their obligation to their fellow scientists does not require them to carry this burden indefinitely. As Orlans tartly observes, "No one can dictate the time of eminent men, and those who prefer their laboratories to Washington presumably remain in them. . . . each man must decide for himself how much time he wants to spend being inquisitive, and how much being influential."[16]

The faults that critics find in the system of government patronage by which American science is so richly nourished are not limited to those I have already discussed—namely, that the system tends to breed entrepreneurs, to discourage imaginative research by young scientists, to intensify competition among scientists, and to take up too much of its beneficiaries' time. Another common criticism is that scientists at a few leading universities get an unfairly large share of the money the government spends to support academic science. In 1965, ten universities got 25 percent of this money. The list was headed by M.I.T., which got $60 million, and included Michigan, U.C.L.A., Columbia, Cornell, Illinois, Berkeley, Stanford, Minnesota, and Harvard. Ten other universities, including Chicago, Pennsylvania, Texas, Wisconsin, and Yale, got 16.5 percent.[17]

Since government agencies are charged with investing their research money where it will yield the largest scientific dividends, the fact that so much of it goes to so few institutions is not in itself evidence that the money is being unfairly distributed. In general, the best scientists with the best ideas are to be found at the universities that pay the highest salaries, attract the best students, and have the greatest prestige—in other words, at universities like Harvard, M.I.T., Michigan, and Illinois. There is no question that the copious flow of government money into universities such as these has enhanced their charms in the eyes of scientists. But these institutions attracted the most distinguished scientists long before there were any government research grants. In 1934, Edwin R. Embree ranked American universities by the number of outstanding scientists on their faculties, and Harvard, with seventy-eight, ranked first. It was followed by Chicago (57), Columbia (54), Yale (50), California (46), Johns Hopkins (39), Cornell (35), Princeton (31), Wisconsin (30), Michigan (29), Minnesota (26), and Stanford (25). Embree did not include M.I.T. or Cal Tech in his survey, but if he had they would unquestionably have ranked high on his list.[18]

It seems clear, however, that scientists at major universities do have a certain unfair advantage in applying for research grants. One reason is that the panels that evaluate their proposals are likely to be made up mainly of professors who teach at the same class of institutions. In 1964, for example, eight of the eleven members of the National Science Foundation's advisory panel for physics were connected with major universities—specifically, with Illinois, Cornell, Indiana, Columbia, Washington (St. Louis), Chicago, Berkeley, and Wisconsin. Under the circumstances, it would be astonishing if there were not some occasional logrolling and nest-feathering. "One wishes," a scientist with long experience as a government adviser wrote Harold Orlans, "that there were no question about the nobility of motive of advisory committees or panels. . . . Unfortunately and sadly I must admit that I have seen much evidence of self-serving, and of small concern for the intellectual advancement of those who haven't emerged as big names."[19] Even if one assumes that panelists try very hard to be fair and objective—which even so skeptical an observer as Orlans grants that they do most of the time—it would be naïve to think that their judgments are invariably untainted by institutional snobbery. Furthermore, when a panelist is confronted with a proposal from a minor university, his tendency to discount its value may be reinforced (often unconsciously) by self-interest. Professor A of Harvard may see merits in a proposal submitted by his old friend, Professor B of Cal Tech (with whom he may hope to place one of his students), that would not be so apparent if the same proposal had been submitted by Professor X of the University of Oklahoma, of whom he has never heard.

This is not the only way in which the cards are stacked against the scientist who teaches at a second- or third-rate university, especially if he is at the beginning of his career. A young assistant professor of, say, chemistry at a minor university is at a disadvantage because unlike his counterparts at Yale or Michigan or Cal Tech he can get little or no money from his own university for equipment or supplies. This may make it impossible for him to do the exploratory research that might persuade a government agency that the work he wants to do is worth supporting.[20] Furthermore, when he draws up a research proposal he may not be able to count on expert help of the sort that is available at a university like Princeton, where the Office of Research Administration stands ready to give "advice with regard to presentational aspects of the proposal, including proper length, necessary amount of detail, and 'sales appeal.' "[21] Even if he writes just as good a proposal as the young Princeton and Harvard scientists with whom he must compete for money, and even if the panelists who review it are quite free of snobbery, he may lose out because his qualifications are in doubt. A panel's job is to consider not only what the author of a proposal wants to do, but also how well he is equipped to do it. When an applicant is only a year or two out of graduate school, and when (as is often the case) the only papers he has published have been written in collaboration with an older scientist, his qualifications are hard to gauge. If he is teaching at a minor university, the panel has to assume that probably he is there only because none of the major universities was sufficiently impressed with his abilities to offer him a job.

Finally, a panel may be satisfied with the ideas and the qualifications of a young scientist, but doubt that he can do a good job of research at the particular university where he is teaching. In 1964, for example, members of the physics department of Trinity University in San Antonio, Texas, an institution that had only recently begun offering a Ph.D. in physics, sent in four research proposals to the National Science Foundation. All were turned down. To find out why, the department's chairman, Charles Burmeister, met with an NSF official, who read him what the reviewers had said about the proposals. "Not a single reviewer questioned the scientific merit of the proposed

work," Burmeister reported later. "However, practically
every reviewer commented on the unfavorable atmosphere
for the pursuit of research which they assumed existed at
Trinity. For instance, it was the opinion of several that our
classroom teaching load was probably too high, that the
number of good graduate students was too few . . . that the
amount of mutual uplift from colleagues was too little, and
that there was probably little administrative support."
Burmeister did not argue that these were not valid reasons
for turning down a proposal; he simply insisted that "the
comments of the reviewers do not depict the atmosphere
for research at Trinity."[22]

Still another objection to the project-grant system is
that it discriminates against young scientists—even those
who teach at leading universities. In the past two or three
years this discrimination has been felt even in the biomedical sciences, a field in which for many years there had
been plenty of money for young and old alike. In early
1967, for example, the Board of Permanent Officers of the
Yale School of Medicine voiced its concern about "the
increasing number of recent instances in which younger
members of our faculty have been informed by the National Institutes of Health that, although their applications
for research support had been given high priority, insuffi-
cient funds were available to activate the grants." The
Board added, "Promising young colleagues in the basic
sciences have been particularly affected."[23] One reason
why young scientists are at a disadvantage is because they
are less likely to have friends on the panels that review
their proposals than are older professors with whom they
must compete for funds. But there is another and probably
more important reason. Assume that a government agency
has received a proposal from Professor X, a man in his
middle forties who can be counted on to turn out two or
three competent, if unexciting papers per year, and who is

asking the agency to continue the support it has given him in the past. And assume, further, that this support has consisted mainly of paying the salaries of four or five students and technicians who work in Professor X's laboratory. If the agency and its scientific advisers have to choose between giving money to Professor X, and giving it to young Assistant Professors Y and Z, the chances are they will give it to Professor X even if his proposal is less interesting than theirs. For one thing, he has academic dependents to be considered. Besides, he has never, so to speak, missed a dividend, whereas Y and Z so far have no real earnings record.*

Finally, it is argued that while the project-grant system may be a good enough way of supporting certain kinds of research, it is nonsense to suppose that really important scientific discoveries can be programmed in advance like a piece of engineering. "In highly speculative research," a well-known chemist, Joseph H. Simons, has written, "it is neither possible nor desirable to write in a proposal the goals sought and the paths to be followed in an effort to reach these goals. The goals cannot be defined in advance, and the twisting paths would not be understood by the officials in Washington or the referees they select to examine the proposal. Isaac Newton could not have stated the laws of

---

* This practice has recently been criticized by the biologist, Bentley Glass, who is now academic vice-president of the State University of New York at Stony Brook. Addressing the 1967 meeting of the Federation of American Societies for Experimental Biology, Glass observed that when the Atomic Energy Commission had tried to cut back on the support it was giving some of its long-time grantees in biology and medicine, there had been such an outcry that the effort had been abandoned, even though "all students of history of science know . . . that most important scientific discoveries and the most significant scientific work is done not by the elders but by young, often very young men." He added, "I do not mean that all senior investigators are dodoes who should be painlessly eliminated. . . . Yet I do challenge the value of a system that continues to pour the largest sums of support of basic research into their hands." [24]

motion as his objective and outlined the means he would
employ to arrive at them. Nor could Albert Einstein have
outlined the principles of relativity in a proposal before
he could obtain permission to begin his studies."[25] The
same point is made in somewhat different terms by a physicist interviewed by Bernice Eiduson: "My feeling is . . .
that every time a man can tell me how many years he is
going to work and how many research assistants he's going
to need, and how much equipment, he's not going to succeed. I can tell you if I'm going to work on gravity now, at
this moment; but I don't know whether I'm going to have
the answer to the problem that I want solved at the end of
one week or four years. Therefore, how can I decide how
many research assistants are necessary to help me with
something I do not even know I'll be working on in the
future? It's impossible! The whole idea is absurd!"[26]

Some critics of the project-grant system think it has so
many flaws that some other means of subsidizing academic
science should be used instead. One alternative would be
for the government to give large sums of money to universities and let them divide it up as they see fit among their
faculty members. This method is understandably favored
by the presidents of some universities that do not get much
money under the present system, and by their representatives in Congress. Institutional, or block, grants are also
favored, however, by some government officials and scientists who have no axes of their own to grind. They consider such grants a useful device for improving the quality
of scientific research and education at second-rank universities—"creating new centers of scientific excellence," as
this is called in government jargon—and as a means of
giving university science departments, excellent and otherwise, some money they can use at their own discretion.

Both the National Science Foundation and the National

Institutes of Health have in fact been making grants for these purposes in recent years. As of mid-1966, seventeen universities—including Purdue, Rutgers, Tulane, and the Universities of Colorado, Florida, Oregon, and Virginia— had received "development" grants from NSF averaging just under $4 million each. And universities now get a sort of annual bonus from NSF and NIH in the form of institutional grants amounting to a percentage of the total amount their faculty members are receiving from these agencies in individual grants. Government agencies may also give money to a department, rather than to an individual professor, to carry out research in a particular area—this is quite common in high-energy physics—or they may support, by a single grant, an interdisciplinary program in which a number of researchers are collaborating.

Substituting block grants for individual grants would have obvious advantages. Professors would spend less time working up research proposals of their own and less time reviewing the proposals of other professors. Presumably they would also be able to get money more quickly.

But most academic scientists, while they may be in favor of more and bigger institutional grants, want them to supplement, not to replace grants to individuals. "Institutional grants have the danger of substituting favoritism and caprice at a local level for the more rational and disinterested judgments of the federal level," David Riesman, a leading student of the sociology of higher education in America, warned a Congressional committee not long ago. "I believe that the outsider is often readier than the insider to recognize ability, even if it is disguised in an abrasive or unpopular professor or instructor." This view is shared by some administrators, one of whom, Clinton D. Cook, dean of faculties at the University of Vermont, was questioned by the same committee as Riesman. "I know that in my own brash youth my occasional sallies at the administration made me less than a favorite with my dean," Cook recalled. "I was a pretty fair chemist and the National Science Foundation and the National Institutes of Health were, I like to think, more perceptive than my dean in recognizing my talents. I am certainly very sure that were it left to him I would have been one of the last to have received funds from an institutional grant. While naturally I am not subject to similar prejudices, I can imagine deans who would be."[27]

On the whole, scientists who want the government to continue providing support in the form of individual grants seem to me to have the better of the argument. Quite apart from his quirks or prejudices, a dean or a department head can be expert in only one small sector of his field, and if he has been a dean or a department head too long he may be out of touch with what is going on even in that sector. Furthermore, while panel members may roll logs now and again, they are fairly well insulated against the kind of pressures to which local academic administrators would be subjected if the distribution of federal research funds were left up to them. Members of panels do not have to live and work with the people whose requests they turn down. When a panel votes on a proposal from a scientist who teaches at, say, Princeton, and there happens to be a Princeton professor on the panel, he is customarily asked to leave the room. Later he can commiserate with a colleague whose proposal has been rejected even if, as may be the case, he privately concurs in the panel's decision.

There is also a danger that institutional grants would come to be dispensed from a pork barrel, with the biggest and juiciest grants going to the institutions with the best lobbyists and the most influential friends in Washington. Already there have been fierce political battles over appropriations for big research facilities. Soon after Lyndon Johnson became president, for example, he had to decide whether to ask Congress for funds with which to build a $120-million machine called a Fixed Field Alternating Gradient synchrotron, or the FFAG, which a group of universities had been urging the government to build near Madison, Wisconsin. Scientists and administrators at other universities wanted the money spent for other purposes, and there was so much lobbying for and against the FFAG that arriving at a decision on its fate—the decision was not to build it—took up more of Johnson's time, or so he later said, than any other nondefense item in the 1965 budget.[28]

Another way of subsidizing academic research is by the method often described as supporting the man instead of the project. This alternative has been advocated by, among others, Merle Tuve, whose comments on the frenzied character of academic life today are quoted at the beginning of this chapter. "I mean thus to say," Tuve has explained, "that we might use public funds to purchase a creative investigator's working lifetime, and then give it back to him to spend in his research efforts. A single lump sum of say $700,000 would pay the remaining lifetime salary of a gifted research man after he has been clearly identified as a creative investigator by the age of thirty or thirty-five, and would pay in addition for one or two technical assistants or two or three students to work with him. . . . If we were to allocate forty to sixty million dollars per year to the creation of such Research Professors or Research Scholars . . . in one decade we would have in this country a solid phalanx of five hundred or six hundred outstanding investigators dedicated to basic research and unquestionably free to devote their personal time and attention to creative ideas for the rest of their lives."[29]

Some American scientists are already beneficiaries of arrangements of this kind. Among them are researchers at a

number of privately endowed research organizations; they
include the Carnegie Institution of Washington, with one
branch of which—the Department of Terrestrial Magnetism—Tuve himself has been associated for many years.
There are also endowed research professorships at many
universities. In 1963, for example, the New York legislature
voted to provide $100,000 a year for each of ten profes-
sorial chairs to be established in the state. One of the first
to be established, the Albert Einstein Chair in Science at
the Stony Brook branch of the State University of New
York, was filled by C. N. Yang, a Nobel prizewinner in
physics who had previously been a professor at the Institute for Advanced Study. Yang's salary is $45,000 a year,
and he is free to use the remaining $55,000 to pay the
salaries of research assistants, or for other purposes related
to his research. The federal government, too, has in effect
endowed a number of research professorships. More than
two hundred investigators in the biomedical sciences, most
of whom are on the faculties of medical schools, have received NIH career awards which guarantee them a salary
of $25,000 a year for the balance of their careers, provided
they devote their full time to research.

After a three-year trial, NIH stopped making career
awards—mainly, it seems, because medical school deans
and department heads objected to the requirement that
recipients be exempted from teaching and administrative
duties.[30] (Administrators are often happy enough to put
up with this sort of thing in the case of a professor who is
bringing in a couple of hundred thousand dollars a year
in grant money; a professor whose dowry consists of only
enough money to pay his own salary is something else
again.) But there are probably several hundred professors
who enjoy, even under the project-grant system, a virtual
guarantee of lifetime support for their research no matter
what they choose to do. A scientist whose attainments

would qualify him for one of Tuve's Research Professor-ships can usually get research grants no matter how vague or even foolish his proposals may seem to a review panel. If he does run into resistance, he need only rewrite his proposal so that it looks as though he knows exactly where he is going and how he is going to get there. This tactical maneuver, often called bootlegging, has been endorsed by such eminent scientists as the late Peter J. W. Debye, win-ner of the 1936 Nobel prize for chemistry. "It is relatively easy to get money, you see, but only for things where you can predict the outcome," Debye told an interviewer in 1965. "And it is not easy to get money for a thing which is wild—where you cannot say 'This is going to have re-sults'. . . . And many of the things which do come out and are good are being done by a certain kind of faking. Oh yes, you do the things that are written down, but you don't do them the way they are written. You use the opportunity to do something different. If something comes out of it, well, everybody is happy."[31]

The project-grant system has so many merits that it would seem more sensible to correct its faults than to do away with it. A number of reforms have been suggested by the National Academy of Science's Committee on Science and Public Policy, a body whose views reflect (and help to shape) the opinions of the leaders of the scientific estab-lishment in America. The committee has proposed, among other things, that government review panels should repre-sent the whole scientific community, not just that portion of it located at universities like Harvard and Berkeley; that terms of service on panels should be short, and that mem-bers should not be eligible for reappointment; and that more young scientists should be appointed to panels. "When some individuals serve too continuously on the panels of one or several agencies," the committee warned, "and when a few universities are regularly over-represented, the burden is too concentrated on the individuals involved and the system is open to the charge of favoritism in judgment."[32]

The committee also proposed that special small research grants be made available to young scientists, who could apply for them simply by outlining their research interests in a general way and submitting letters of endorsement from older scientists personally acquainted with their work. (Some scientists feel such grants should be made almost automatically. "Maybe at some modest level you should support everything," George Carpenter told me. "That way you won't have forced a young man at the bravest part of his life, at that everything-to-gain, nothing-to-lose stage, that delicate stage, that embryonic stage— you won't have forced him to fall into a rut.") Finally, the committee suggested ways of cutting down the time that scientists have to spend getting and administering grants. It proposed that grants be made for longer periods; that government agencies require fewer and simpler progress reports; and that grantees be allowed to use funds that have been allocated for equipment and supplies pretty much as they see fit, without having to get permission from Washington to buy a Type B instrument, for example, when the budget accompanying their original proposal specified a Type A.

The committee said nothing about one feature of the present system that many scientists dislike—that is, the government's use of research grants as a means of subsidizing graduate education. A strong plea for the discontinuation of this practice was recently made by Gilbert Stork, a professor of chemistry at Columbia, who told a Congressional committee that the government should make separate grants to university science departments to support "the graduate students who are in training without making their training dependent on half-hearted research involvement by their sponsors." Stork said this would "permit serious financial support to be accorded to the best research only, without the concern that to do so might deprive well-qualified students of support they need."[33]

In the summer of 1963, an anonymous contributor to the English magazine *New Scientist*, on returning to England after spending a year at "one of the most reputable institutions in North America," recorded his disillusionment with American science. "It is alarming," he wrote, "to see how many papers are published in the journals merely as a re-hash of some previously published piece of work; it is sad to see how much creative energy now goes into the polishing of applications for grants from public funds; it is appalling that people can be so ready to do each other down, or to win the patronage of those powerful creatures who staff the committees in Washington; it is upsetting to see how mean people can be to each other in the frightful competition for priority. . . . personal success in science has come to demand the qualities traditionally thought necessary for success in selling vacuum cleaners."[34]

As I have tried to show, there is some truth in these accusations. The question is, How much? One way to get at the answer is to consider the quality of the work done by American scientists over the last ten or fifteen years. As recently as the 1930's, the United States, for all its glittering techological achievements, was essentially an adapter and consumer of European science. One hundred and three Nobel prizes for science were awarded between 1901 and 1940, and Americans won or shared in only ten of these. By contrast, eighteen of the thirty-three prizes awarded in 1956 through 1965, including eight of the eleven prizes in physics, were either shared or won outright by Americans; of the others, eight were shared or won by Englishmen, four by Germans, and four by Russians.

This does not in itself prove, of course, that the United States has become the best place for gifted scientists to work. Many of the Nobel prizes of recent years have been given for work done well before World War Two. (Peyton Rous, of Rockefeller University, who shared the 1966 prize in medicine or physiology with Charles Huggins of the University of Chicago, received the award at least in part because of a discovery—that a virus can cause cancer in chickens—that he made in 1911.) But it is clear that in a number of fields, including elementary-particle physics, quantum electronics, observational astrophysics, and some branches of molecular biology, the best work in recent years more often than not has been done in the United States. This is also true of mathematics. In a paper written in 1965 at the request of the House Committee on Science and Astronautics, Saunders MacLane, a professor of mathematics at the University of Chicago, pointed out that for some ten years after the end of World War Two the world's best young mathematicians were being produced by France. He added, however, that "in the decade 1955–64, the United States (and perhaps Russia) leads in this regard." MacLane noted that because of the nature of mathematical work such judgments are easy to make. "Mathematics abounds in famous unsolved problems," he wrote. "[T]he man who finally solves one usually does so not by dint of apparatus, but by harder or more effective and courageous thought. . . . In these regards, mathematics in the United States has recently been strikingly successful."* The high quality of chemical research in the United

---

* My impression is that such judgments are likely to be quite free of ethnocentric bias. American scientists often exaggerate the achievements of people in their own universities or departments, but have little tendency to be chauvinistic about American as opposed to European science.

States is indicated by the fact that the work of American investigators tends to be cited in chemical journals published outside the United States more often than the work of investigators in any other country.[35]

This change has come about partly because of the damage done to European science by the war, and partly because of the enormous contributions made by distinguished European scientists who came to the United States as refugees from Hitler and Mussolini.[36] But there is no question that the vitality of American science has also been due in large measure to the nature and the extent of the support the United States government has given to basic scientific research. Many European scientists are inclined to attribute this vitality to the relative ease with which a talented young scientist in the United States can find the time and means to do research in areas of his own choosing. This view would appear to be held by, among others, the distinguished Russian physicist, Pyotr Kapitsa, who is head of the Soviet Academy's Institute of Physical Problems. Writing in *Komsomolskaya Pravda*, the Communist party youth newspaper, Kapitsa warned in early 1966 that "in the past few years the scientific gap between our country and the U.S. has not been closed," and implied that the main trouble with Soviet science was that too many research jobs were held by incompetent older scientists. "It would, for example, be possible to transfer fifteen to twenty percent of our staffs from science to industry every year," he wrote, "and to take into research well-prepared and qualified youth. In this manner, we would improve the quality of scientific staffs and also not close the door of science in the face of the young."[37]

The advantages that young scientists enjoy in the United States are also emphasized in a recent review of biomedical research in Western Europe. The authors note "the virtual absence of competitive grant mechanisms," and observe that consequently "it is difficult for the young but experienced European investigator to develop an independent research program or pursue his own research ideas. He is usually totally dependent financially upon his professor or institute director, and therefore often obliged to follow prescribed research paths." In addition, they point out, jobs equivalent to those of an assistant or an associate professor are very rare in Europe, and "these two circumstances conspire to create a black and frustrating career prospect for the young biomedical scientist in Europe."

The authors of the report describe the situation of biomedical scientists in America as it is viewed by the thousands of young Europeans who have spent a year or two in medical school laboratories and biomedical research institutes in the United States. "They have been exposed to what, for many, is a radically different and liberating atmosphere in medical research and education," they write, "and this has often been the most important and persisting part of their experience." They add that this atmosphere is sometimes referred to as the "American approach." As viewed by young Europeans, its most valuable elements include early independence for young investigators, informal relations between students and professors, freedom to move from one institution to another, and "absence of academic hierarchism."[38]

The United States has strong attractions for English scientists too, and the chance to earn higher pay is only one reason why so many have migrated to America in recent years. Some of the other reasons were set forth by the magazine *Réalités* in 1964, in a report on an interview with a thirty-five-year-old English chemist who had spent several months as a visitor at Berkeley and who was about to leave England to become a professor there. "I am not saying that I find the prospect of a more comfortable way of life is painful," he was quoted as saying, "but it is certainly not the twenty percent salary increase that has decided me to take the leap." The main thing, he said, was his conviction that if he stayed in England he might never be able to do the kind of scientific work he felt capable of doing. "We're bogged down in a university hierarchy that hasn't changed since Queen Victoria—and is proud of the fact," he said. "So I'm answerable to a respectable professor who, unfortunately for him, wasn't given charge of his laboratory till he was over fifty. . . . If I stayed on here the same thing would happen to me. I'd become my own master at about the same age, but then I'd be worried about my faculties being past their peak." He said that he would be directing his own laboratory at Berkeley, and that in his opinion the chance to be independent at an early age was the main thing that was drawing European scientists to America. All over the Continent, he said, "you find the same sort of material and intellectual bottlenecks curbing research, you find the same attitude towards science, which is still regarded as a poor relation. . . . Clearly the United States today has a magnetic attraction for scientists—somewhat like the attraction Italy and France held for artists and writers in the past."[39]

One may assume that such rapture will be followed by a certain amount of disillusionment. The tone of scientific undertakings in America has unquestionably been coarsened by the corruption that is inevitable in human affairs when money and power are at stake. But the enthusiasm for American ways that many young European scientists display nevertheless seems more to the point than the bitterness of the *New Scientist*'s anonymous correspondent. The most striking thing about basic science in America since World War Two is not how much it has been corrupted by money, but how little.

V

The Styles of Big Science

ONE OF THE most significant changes in science over the last quarter of a century has been the rapid evolution of a new way of doing scientific research. Its basic elements are not unlike those of factory production. "Just as the modern corporation has supplanted free partnership and apprenticeship in industry," the sociologist Warren Hagstrom has pointed out, "so a more complex form of organization may be supplanting free collaboration and the professor-student association in science. Both changes involve the development of a more complex division of labor, the separation of the worker from the tools of production, and the greater centralization of authority."[1]

The change has been most striking in physics. Before 1940, performing a physical experiment was almost as personal an undertaking as writing an essay. Melvin Schwartz, a physicist who has recently been doing experiments on the new accelerator at Stanford University, has written nostalgically of the days when a professor and his graduate students would build with their own hands all the equipment they needed. "Rare was the experimenter and graduate student who did not know every nut and bolt in the apparatus," Schwartz recalls. "This knowledge was essential during the many hours of 'bug-picking' when nothing worked properly. Its compensation was the enormous feel-

134

ing of pride when the apparatus did in fact work! Next came the 'run'—an almost mystical experience in the life of many a graduate student. For the first time in his life he was gathering data—often data that was new and unique in the body of human knowledge." After this, Schwartz continues, came the "many weeks of thoughtful analysis during which one [attempted] to understand the results of the experiment, analyze possible biases, and relate the result to the remainder of human understanding." He concludes, "Through the entire course of this idealized investigation would normally flow the spirit of independent, original thought. If an experiment failed one had no one to blame but oneself. If it succeeded the success was a very personal matter."[2]

There are areas of physics in which experiments are still done this way. But they do not include high-energy particle physics. In this field the aim is to gain an understanding of the fundamental structure of matter by studying what happens when atomic nuclei are bombarded with protons or electrons that are traveling at very nearly the speed of light. To generate a beam of such particles requires machines that cost huge sums of money—a new accelerator that is to be built at Weston, Illinois, is expected to cost around $400 million—and are much too complicated for a professor and one or two graduate students to operate. "I'd be helpless doing it all by myself, really helpless," a Nobel laureate in physics has said. "You look at the bevatron set up and you realize that you would have to tie up so much equipment over such a long time in order to set it all up yourself. You certainly can't run the thing twenty hours a day yourself. . . . It takes a crew of three just to keep the thing working on a routine basis and keep plotting the graphs and writing down the data. It takes more when something a little more drastic has to be done. One person has to look in the machine, another person has to move something under instructions. The least one needs . . . is roughly three Ph.D. people and six students. This is rather minimal. . . ."[3] Papers reporting the results of experiments in high-energy physics have in some instances carried the names, as authors, of more than thirty persons.

The lengths to which division of labor has been carried in high-energy physics may be illustrated by the operations of a group led by a prominent experimental physicist named Luis W. Alvarez. Alvarez is a professor at the University of California, and the accelerator his group has used for its experiments is the $30-million bevatron at the Lawrence Radiation Laboratory in Berkeley. The group also uses a device called a bubble chamber, in which the path of a subatomic particle can be traced by the bubbles it makes as it passes through liquid hydrogen.

Alvarez built the first large bubble chamber in the 1950's; and he proposed, and his group developed, the methods (now used by many other groups as well as his) whereby the enormous quantity of data that a big chamber can produce, in the form of photographs of bubble tracks, can be semiautomatically processed. This processing is done by using special machines that permit technicians known as scanners to measure the length, angle, and curvature of each bubble track, and to punch the information onto a paper tape. The information is automatically transferred to a magnetic tape, and a computer then calculates and tabulates basic data needed for the analysis of the nuclear reactions that the tracks show to have taken place.

When I talked with Alvarez in 1965 there were more than two hundred people in his group. Twenty-three were physicists with Ph.D.'s; some of these had faculty appointments at the University of California, others were spending a year or two at the Radiation Laboratory as postdoctoral researchers, and still others were permanent members of the laboratory staff. The group also included twenty graduate students working for their doctorates, and one hundred and seventy film-scanners, computer programmers, engineers, and assorted technicians.

The work of the group is organized around so-called beam runs—periods of six months to a year during which a proton beam having certain specified characteristics is focused on a number of different targets. As a rule, only fifteen to twenty of the physicists and graduate students in the group work on a particular beam run; the others analyze data from the previous run or plan the next one. "Making the beam is a big effort," Alvarez said. "This is the point where the physicists in this business come closest to really handling the apparatus. Building the beam requires constant testing and computer analysis. This work takes a lot of time. Some people like this work; others hate it." While some members of a subgroup work on the beam, others prepare detailed instructions for the scanners. Still others write programs for the computer that will process the bubble-chamber data. When the beam is in operation, the graduate students take turns at monitoring its performance. They, and the older physicists with whom they work, also spend a great deal of time rescanning photographs that have been picked out by the computer. The data that is taken from the photographs is divided up according to a prearranged plan. Some people, for instance, study how certain events vary from one energy level to another—the energy of the beam is usually varied in the course of a run—while others analyze the relations between different kinds of events occurring at the same energy level. On the average, Alvarez said, a beam run yields data for from ten to twenty scientific papers.

Alvarez's role is rather like that of the classical entrepreneur, as portrayed in an elementary economics text. He tries to combine capital and labor in such a way as to produce goods, in the form of marketable scientific data and discoveries, in large quantities and at the lowest possible cost. Alvarez is an exceptionally able and inventive scientist, and at first, when the enterprise was relatively small, he made all the scientific decisions himself. "I decided what techniques should be used," he said. "I decided what experiments we would run, and what our general strategy should be." As time passed, however, he began to operate less like a nineteenth-century capitalist and more like a twentieth-century professional manager. "We've undergone a smooth transition to autonomy," he said. "The younger people suggest the experiments now. They know much better than I do what should be done. As head of the group, the most important thing I do now is put out fires. Members of my group are always getting good offers to go somewhere else, and I have to do what I can to keep them here. It would be very easy for us to go into an autocatalytic decline. Last month, one of my best young men had good offers from Illinois and Maryland. Those raids were countered by an accelerated promotion in academic rank here at Berkeley. We've trained a lot of competitors who have a lot of money to spend now—we taught both Illinois and Maryland how to get into this business—and they'd love to spend it on members of my group."

Like a corporation president or a political leader, Alvarez also has to deal with conflicts among his lieutenants. Often these involve disagreements over who is to have the privilege of analyzing and writing up a particular set of data. "You're dealing with high-spirited, prima-donna type people," Alvarez said. "The difficulty arises when something new and exciting shows up, something you hadn't anticipated finding. Remember, these are tough-minded characters, interested in furthering their own careers. The question is, who is to get the goodies? In the early days, we solved the problem by putting everyone's name on the papers describing the windfalls, but that won't work now."

From the standpoint of a student, as I have suggested, belonging to a group like Alvarez's may have serious disadvantages. One is that the graduate students have to do a great deal of routine and boring work. Another is that their training as researchers is often very narrow, a point emphasized by Melvin Schwartz. A student who is getting his doctorate as a member of a bubble-chamber group, Schwartz writes, "is essentially reduced to a card shuffler and graph plotter, at least until these chores can be automatized too." He adds, "Rare is the student who knows what the bubble chamber looks like, and rarer yet the student who can operate one."[4] In the opinion of another physicist, who heads a bubble-chamber group at a midwestern university, good students can learn a lot by doing bubble-chamber work, but they may have to fight the system to do so. "Students do well if they're aggressive," he says. "If they don't trust anything, if they won't take your word for anything—if they're willing to check it out, and make sure for themselves, and improve on what you give them, then they will get the kind of experience a student should have. But if they're willing to just sit back and let the established systems process the data for them, and then pick up at the last stage, the analysis stage—well, I think there certainly are some of those, very likely too many of them." Many very able students who are attracted by the intellectual prizes at stake in experimental high-energy physics are put off by the idea of group research, and elect to work in a field such as solid-state physics, where experiments can be done in the traditional way. This tendency has been remarked by, among others, Robert Hofstadter, an experimental high-energy physicist who shared a Nobel prize in 1961. "The joyous feeling of individual accomplishment is no longer attainable," he has said, "and many of our best young scientists are avoiding this type of research."[5]

There is also a premium in group research on being articulate and cocky. (A successful high-energy physicist, to whom both these adjectives apply, told me, "You can't get anywhere in this business unless you're an operator.") A scientist who is diffident, politically inept, or incapable of arguing forcefully and persuasively for his ideas may do very well in other areas of research. But he is most unlikely ever to become the head of a group like Alvarez's, and if he goes into high-energy physics he may end up as a high-level technician—someone who is consulted on certain phases of the planning and execution of experiments, but who does not initiate experiments himself.

This is not to suggest that people who end up as high-level technicians in accelerator groups would necessarily have flourished as independent investigators if they had gone into some other field of research. "We try not to cast many of our Ph.D. holders into the role of technicians," Alvarez told me, "but we are not completely successful in this, since some people are less self-motivating than others, and are more content to do some of the chores that are required to keep a large group operating." Group research has the merit of providing useful and interesting work for people who may not be equipped, temperamentally or intellectually, to do research of real significance on their own. Many of these people, if they had been born twenty or thirty years earlier, would probably not have become scientists at all. In an essay on "Teamwork and Individual Research," Leo Kowarski, a physicist associated with the European Organization for Nuclear Research, points out that "with the great increase in the number of scientific posts which has occurred in the last twenty years, an ever growing number of young people have a chance of doing pure scientific research." He goes on to argue that if this were not the case, team research would be much harder to organize. "The proportion of individual creative minds goes down," he writes, "but that of research workers willing to accept the constraints of team work goes up, and it is admittedly easier to do science in this way now than it was thirty years ago, since it suits better the common run of people."[6]

There are other fields besides high-energy physics in which research is now commonly done by teams of scientists whose work is directed or coordinated by a leader. This is largely true, for example, in plasma physics, in radio astronomy, and in the atmospheric sciences, where the instruments needed for making experiments and observations are, like particle accelerators, too big and complicated for one man to handle, even with the help of two or three graduate students. In addition, many scientists are engaged in the kind of group research in which the skills of people trained in several different disciplines are brought to bear on a problem, or a set of related problems. This is very common in the so-called materials sciences, and in certain branches of biomedical research. In some cases, the collaboration is of the traditional kind, in which two or three scientists join forces, often for a fairly short period, to work on a problem of common interest. But many scientists engaged in interdisciplinary projects are members of more or less permanent groups whose course is set for them by a leader. Such a group may include people whom Warren Hagstrom refers to as professional technicians. These people have doctorates, often in electron microscopy or statistics. But Hagstrom argues that the designation of technician is justified because they "are not expected to make research decisions or to be committed to the solution of scientific problems." He adds, "Instead they are expected to solve the problems others give them, and they do so for money and not for recognition in the scientific community. In other words, the professional technician, like most workers in modern society, is capable of alienating himself from his work."[7]

Still another form of group effort, which is frequently mounted by biochemists, involves putting together a sort of human machine to collect data and perform certain laboratory operations. Groups that have been organized for this purpose are most often found in medical schools, and they usually include, in addition to their leader, one or two junior faculty members, a few technicians, and from ten to thirty young men and women with M.D.'s or Ph.D.'s, who are completing their training as researchers. From the leader's standpoint, the advantage of having so many highly skilled apprentices is that by assigning them such tasks as, for example, synthesizing certain kinds of compounds over and over again, he can complete in a few months experimental procedures that might otherwise take ten or fifteen years. This technique has obvious limitations. The act of imagination by which a significant new theory or concept is produced cannot very well be programmed in advance for a group operation. But there are important problems that can be handled efficiently, once a new theory or concept has pointed the way to their solution, by breaking them down into a number of smaller problems, and parceling these out to the members of a team.

The mixed feelings that many scientists have about doing things this way may be illustrated by a talk I had with a young biochemist named *Norman Berringer*, who has made very important contributions to the understanding of genetic processes. Berringer got his Ph.D. in 1957, spent two years as a postdoctoral fellow at a large government laboratory, and then became a member of the laboratory's permanent staff. He decided to study how proteins are synthesized, and although research in this field was dominated by big groups, he started out working entirely by himself.

After a year or so he took on one postdoctoral associate, with whose help he perfected a technique that cleared the way for a systematic attack on the genetic code, the language in which instructions for the synthesis of particular proteins are transmitted. "It was like walking into a toy store," Berringer told me. "There were a hundred beautiful problems you could work on. But right away the major laboratories in the field all zoomed in, and I felt I either had to get out of the field—there were just two of us, and we couldn't compete with the big machines that were all geared up and rolling—or build some sort of machine myself. I chose to expand my group enough so that we could at least work on one or two selected problems in a competitive way."

Young scientists both in the United States and abroad were eager to come and work with Berringer, and before long he was supervising the work of twelve postdoctoral fellows and four technicians. "It's very exciting to have a group like this, and very productive," he recalled. "But the post-docs really need direction, and the information is piling in faster than you can deal with it, and you only have so much time. So you cut down on your reading, you accumulate twenty pounds of unanswered mail, you cut down on the time when you're free to think. You don't have time to play with ideas. I finally decided I was being overproductive." At this point Berringer had stopped taking on new postdoctoral researchers, and when I talked with him he had only five working in his laboratory. As they left for other jobs, Berringer said, he planned to spend more and more of his time feeling his way into a new field

of research: neurobiology. "This means I will be unproductive for perhaps three or four years," he said. "You can't
do this if you have a lot of postdoctorals. You can only
move into an entirely new field if you travel light. You
have to be a sort of vagabond. I've decided I don't really
want to direct anything."

Berringer said that although he himself did not like running a big research group, he thought that for a young
biochemist it could be a very good experience to spend a
couple of years in a group such as his. "If things work out,
a person not only learns an immense amount, but he may
have a chance to do beautiful work," he said. "Some of the
people who have gone through my laboratory have had
superb opportunities. Those who were good, or lucky, the
ones who were put on a problem that broke with a re-
sounding bang, were propelled right into upper-echelon
jobs." Berringer conceded that for one period of six or
eight months much of the group's effort had had to go into
the laborious preparation of certain materials, and that this
had been discouraging to some people. "Two of the fellows
disliked this intensely," he said. "They thought they were
being used as peons. But their perspective was wrong. We
didn't need them just to provide hands. The work required
brains and imagination, and people had a magnificent opportunity to carve out whatever they wanted to carve out.
There's nothing wrong with being in a group if you pick a
lab where you can learn important techniques, where you
can work closely with the senior investigator, and where
you will have a chance to help shape things intellectually."

Some successful biochemists who run big groups do look
on their postdoctoral researchers as hired hands rather than
as junior partners in a common enterprise. Able young scientists sometimes choose to apprentice themselves to such
men because they have dreams of running a big group of
their own some day, and want to learn how it is done. A

Belgian-born biochemist, now on the faculty of a leading
American medical school, told me that he had chosen to do his
postdoctoral work as a member of a very large group even
though he knew that the man he would be working for was
more concerned with outproducing his competitors than
with developing the talents of the average researcher who
passed through his laboratory. "I wanted to see what
makes a big shot tick," he said. "I knew that in a group like
his you run the risk of being caught up in a machine. But I
was convinced that you can't keep a good man down, and I
managed to avoid this fate. Not everyone is equally successful. In the end, though, a big shot will be able to place
you in a good job even if you are rather mediocre."

The bubble chamber, which has become a symbol of
assembly-line research, was invented in 1952 by a young
Berkeley professor, Donald Glaser, who has said that he
got the idea for it while gazing into a glass of beer. Some
years later, a physicist named Arthur Roberts, who is an
accomplished musician and balladeer, commemorated the
event in a song called "The Birth of the Bubble Chamber
—a Moralistic Drinking Song." The final stanza goes, in
part:

SOLO: The bubble chamber now is made of sterner stuff
than beer.
It's run by corporations huge on megabucks per
year.
The magnets pulse, the cameras click, the IBM's
they chatter,
Vast cohorts grind the answers out: some do,
some do not matter.

CHORUS: Let us not inquire into that matter.

SOLO: So all who love the wild surmise, the mad con-
jecture free,
Who do not like research in groups of more than
twenty-three,

> Remember still the theorem that Glaser proved
> again—
> To hell with organization man—there's nothing
> like a brain . . .[8]

The attitude these lines convey is by no means shared by all physicists. Many of the younger ones find research with accelerators and bubble chambers very much to their liking. A physicist in his late twenties, who got his Ph.D. at Columbia in 1964 and is now the leader of a small group doing bubble-chamber experiments at a midwestern university, told me that he sees no great difference between what he does and what physicists have done in the past. "Sure, I work with a lot more people," he said. "But each of us works on a different part of a big problem. We're not always having meetings, like the board of directors of General Motors, and doing things as a group. The individual has a lot of chance to express himself." He conceded that he was perhaps unusually fortunate in this respect. "I don't think any of the people who were in my group at Columbia has as much independence where he is now as I have," he said. "My friend at——says he works with a very domineering professor. Still, he's the only one in his group who can analyze an experiment, and therefore when they get to that point he will be able to exert a lot of influence over the way things are done. I know somebody who is down at——. He feels he's got a lot of independence. A proposal they are going to make to Brookhaven follows his suggestions despite the fact that there are three full professors in the group. Most of the people I know are fairly happy in what they are doing. They feel they have enough room to exercise the initiative they want to."

But physicists who, like Roberts, began their careers before World War Two are inclined to feel that younger men are cheerful about the constraints of group research only because they have never known anything else. When older physicists reflect on how things were when they were young, before physics had become a big business, it is usually with a sense of loss. Even those who have made highly effective use of big machines and big research teams are often unhappy about a style of research that they complain has been forced on them by technological necessity. "I'm a gadgeteer at heart," Alvarez told me. "I don't want to spend all my life sitting at a desk reading computer printouts. This sort of group research is unavoidable in a field where you gain so much by being part of a group. But it's not really a good way of life for anyone who wants to experience the thrill of personal achievement that was for so long the scientist's main reward."

Moreover, it is not only middle-aged physicists, yearning for a lost Eden, who dislike and fear group research. Many scientists are afraid that the bubble-chamber and the twenty-three-man team are harbingers of a future in which there will be no place for people who will not (or can not) conform to the requirements of socialized research.

Thus when Alvin Weinberg, director of the Oak Ridge National Laboratory, recently suggested that a little more group research might be a good thing in the biological sciences, he could count on the fact that most biologists would not take kindly to the idea. Weinberg, a physicist who often writes about the relations between science and public policy, and whose views are generally respected by other scientists, has himself been an outspoken critic of big and costly scientific enterprises. ("The big scientific community," he once wrote, "tends to acquire more and more bosses. The Indians with bellies to the bench are hard to discern for all the chiefs with bellies to the mahogany desks."[9]) But at a symposium on biomedical research, in 1965, he noted that "Big Scientists from neighboring fields have taught the sin of Big Science to the biologists," and went on to explain why he thought this was a good thing. "Perhaps the best known example of the drastically changed style of some biological research is the large-scale mouse genetics experiment of W. L. Russell at Oak Ridge," he said. "For the past sixteen years Russell has been studying the genetic effects of ionizing radiation in a mammal, the mouse. Since mutations even at high dose rates are so rare, Russell uses colonies containing 100,000 mice. To perform such experiments takes much money and many people; and yet it seems impossible to visualize any other way of obtaining the data."[10]

Weinberg urged biologists "to expand even at the cost of individual effectiveness as long as their total output increases; to break down the traditional disciplinary barriers . . . to overcome their suspicion of the physical scientists; in short, to accept the new style of Big Science in addition to the old style of Little Science." Acknowledging that "traditional biologists must surely recoil in horror at the advice I give them," he went on to say: "But before they throw me out bodily (an impulse that visions of larger research budgets ought to restrain), I remind them that insofar as what they do is part of the war against human suffering, their desires and tastes are not all that matter. Biomedical science is not done, or most importantly, not supported by the public simply because it gives intense satisfaction to the dedicated and successful biomedical researcher. It is supported on a really large scale because out of it has come means of eliminating man's infirmities. If a style that complements the traditional style is needed in order to mount a much larger biomedical research enterprise, then this style will have to be adopted much as it hurts the sensibilities of the traditionalists."

Resistance to proposals like Weinberg's springs in part from a natural wish to cling to pleasant and familiar ways. Walter Rosenblith, a professor of biophysics at M.I.T., noted in an article in *Daedalus* a few years ago that "throughout the entire realm of science new organizational arrangements, new practices, new temperaments and new motivations are proliferating." He continued, "It is, of course, perfectly possible for scientists to decide by fiat that these new-fangled trappings are not science, that as a matter of fact they have nothing to do with science, and that the term 'science' applies only to those activities that have undergone relatively few changes since the times of Newton and Maxwell. It is questionable whether at this stage of the history of science such an attitude is realistic in terms of the social role that has devolved upon science and its practitioners."[11]

But even scientists who concede that group research is quite appropriate in certain areas are afraid it will spread to areas where it is not appropriate at all. They are worried that the public may become so infatuated with massive, interdisciplinary efforts that it will neglect the needs of scientists who work without big teams or big machines. This danger has been pointed out by, among others, George Kistiakowsky, a Harvard chemistry professor who served for three years as President Eisenhower's scientific adviser, and who is recognized by politicians (and by other scientists) as a leading spokesman for university scientists. In a statement submitted to a House committee in 1963, Kistiakowsky said it was important, of course, for Congress to support the kind of research in which big teams and expensive facilities are indispensable. "I am concerned, however," he said, "that perhaps the balance has swung too far in this direction; the great strength of American science has been the individual scientist with a small group of collaborators. If this support is denied in the future because of tighter overall limitation of funds and greater glamour of large undertakings, I fear that much of real value in American science will be lost."[12] The question is whether Little Science and Big Science can coexist, or whether stubborn, prickly nonconformists, who have been responsible for so many important discoveries, will in time be barred from scientific laboratories, or be tolerated only as quaint anachronisms.

One possible cause for alarm in this connection is the increase in collaboration among scientists. A sociologist, Harriet Zuckerman, who analyzed the authorship of papers in leading American scientific journals found that only 28 percent of the papers printed in the 1950's were signed by a single author, as compared with 56 percent in the 1920's. Over the same thirty years, the percentage of papers signed by four or more authors rose steeply. In biochemistry, the increase was from 2 to 12 percent; in physics, it was from zero to 7 percent.[13]

But Little Science is still flourishing. Even in the 1950's, three out of four papers in the journals sampled by Miss Zuckerman were signed by one or two persons. Most scientists on university faculties still work by themselves, or with small groups of students. A survey in 1962 at the University of California at Berkeley indicated that this was true of three out of four mathematicians and statisticians, four out of five biologists, and six out of seven chemists.[14] Even in physics, there have been plenty of opportunities, notably in solid-state research, for people who decide in graduate school that they don't want to work with big machines. (Although Berkeley is an important center of research in high-energy physics, half of the physicists covered by the 1962 survey said they worked by themselves or with students only.) In biochemistry, there are so many openings for young researchers that a scientist can get his postdoctoral training in as big or small a group as he likes.

Traditional modes of doing research also prevail even in some fields where scientists have to use very expensive equipment. The two-hundred-inch telescope at Mount

Palomar in California, the largest in the world, is built so that it can be operated with the help of just one technician, and astronomers who use this enormous piece of machinery are allotted a certain number of nights each year during which they are free to use it for any purpose they choose, much as though they were biologists using a dissecting microscope. Oceanographic vessels as a rule are shared by individual scientists working on individual projects. Most oceanographers are affiliated with laboratories, like Columbia University's Lamont Geological Observatory, which operate oceangoing ships, and when they want certain data collected they simply ask that it be gathered for them. Although the director of an oceanographic laboratory is very likely to receive more such requests than he can grant, he cannot afford to be arbitrary or capricious in dealing with them. A young associate professor of geology who teaches at a university that has a big oceanographic laboratory explained to me why this is so. If the director of his laboratory were to deny the use of its deep-sea vessels to good men with good ideas, he said, the good men would go somewhere else, the quality of the laboratory's work would fall off, and eventually the ships, both of which are on loan from government agencies, would be assigned to other institutions. "Our experience has been that no young man has been deprived of the right to do what he wants," he added. "The director needs good young men even more than they need him."

The danger warned of by Kistiakowsky is nevertheless real. As I have pointed out, the government's appropriations for basic research have risen very little in the past three years, even though the cost of doing research, and the number of researchers, have both been increasing quite rapidly. Money to continue existing programs has generally been forthcoming, but it has not been so easy for scientists starting out in academic careers to get grants of

their own. In 1964 and 1965, for example, the National
Science Foundation provided funds for only 7 percent of
the proposals from new investigators in physics that NSF's
scientific advisers had judged to be worth supporting.[15]
This has meant that instead of being able to work on their
own, many young physicists have had to join research
groups headed by older colleagues—or, if already members of such groups, to remain a part of them longer than
they would like.

Moreover, Congress has shown no disposition to help
Little Scientists by diverting to them any of the money
that is going into large-scale projects in the fields of public
health, space, and weaponry, even when there are serious
doubts as to how wisely some of this money is being spent.
In 1965, for instance, a committee made up mainly of scientists, businessmen, and university presidents, which had
been appointed by President Kennedy to study the operations of the National Institutes of Health, was quite critical
of the NIH's $20-million-a-year Cancer Chemotherapy
Program. The committee, reflecting a view held by many
medical scientists, observed that while the government had
already spent nearly $200 million on the program, which
has involved testing more than 100,000 chemical agents for
possible effectiveness against cancer, "NIH has not made
a convincing case for [its] direction and magnitude." The
program had been undertaken, the committee said, without "any very extensive attempts, involving either pilot
tests or analyses, to compare the value of the probable
results with the value of the results that a similar expendi-
ture might have been expected to produce in other biomedical research: by just lifting the over-all level of the
traditional research grant, for example." The committee
recommended that the chemotherapy program be carefully reviewed by an impartial body, with the aim of determining whether it should be modified or perhaps ter-

minated."[16] As of mid-1967, however, the program was still going along pretty much as before.

The position of scientists who want to pursue their own ideas and to work by themselves or with small groups of students is further threatened by a feeling in Washington that perhaps the government has been slightly oversold on the value of free and undirected basic research. The point has been made explicitly by President Johnson, who warned biomedical scientists in 1966 that basic research was all very well, but that the time had come to pay more attention to translating the results of such research into practical benefits.[17]

There is something to be said for this. As Weinberg has argued, there might well be a net gain, in terms of the ability to control disease, if more effort were put into well-conceived and well-managed biomedical research projects with practical, or semipractical objectives, in which the techniques of Big Science would be employed. Little Science is not necessarily good science, and money for scientific investigations of the traditional variety has been so plentiful in the biological sciences in recent years that even people of marginal talent have been able to get grants. Much biomedical research has been trivial and redundant.

But it is harder to spend money wisely for applied than for basic research. Applied research is, by and large, carried out by organizations. And even when members of a large research team start out with the feeling that they have an important mission, they often lose that feeling and end up doing research not because they think it is important, but as a ritual. Researchers who work by themselves can also lose the ability to do good work. But it is easier to stop giving money to an individual than to an organization. This point was emphasized by the committee that studied the operations of NIH. Arguing that "even under the most skillful management the effective productivity of a scientist involved in a large collaborative program will frequently be low," the committee said that NIH should be very wary of undertaking new large-scale programs. In general, the committee wrote, "whether it is a question of the development of a new guided missile or of a new medical cure, prudent use of material and human resources requires that the 'high risk' speculative and exploratory activities be carried out to the greatest possible extent at the basic research level, where the size of the effort required is small."[18]

Such counsels may prevail. Little Science is strongly championed by most of the scientists who, like Kistiakowsky, are regularly consulted by Washington on matters of science policy. Many of these men began their careers before the war and are strongly attached to the traditional modes of scientific research. So are most of the younger scientists at universities and research institutes with whom I have talked. But it seems inevitable that more and more scientists who become influential in Washington will be men inclined by both experience and temperament to prefer big projects. (Doubtless some of them, like many scientists who manage industrial laboratories, will tend to the view that most academic research is self-indulgent puttering.) While these scientists may approve of big government outlays for basic research, they are likely to favor investigations that are organized and managed like applied-research projects. This can scarcely be encouraging to scientists who do not like research in groups of more than twenty-three.

VI

Scientists Without Students

As RECENTLY as 1940, perhaps 90 percent of all basic scientific research in the United States was done by professors, or by students working under their direction. Today there are tens of thousands of basic researchers who are neither students nor teachers—unless they happen to take courses on the side, or to teach after hours, as a form of moonlighting. Most of these scientists work in industry; their careers, and the careers of the much larger number of industrial scientists who do applied research, will be examined in Chapter VIII. But there are also thousands of people like Norman Berringer, who do basic research in government and private laboratories and research institutes. In this chapter, I shall say something about these scientists, and about the institutional habitats in which they have chosen to work.

Robert d'Autremont, a thirty-six-year-old microbiologist, is on the staff of a large, privately endowed research institute whose members include a number of the world's most distinguished biological and medical scientists. A few years ago, the Institute, as it is usually referred to by the people who work there, began awarding doctorates in biology, and d'Autremont's formal job title is Assistant Professor. But the Institute's faculty is more than twice as large as its student body, and he has no formal educational responsibilities of any kind.

Like many biomedical researchers, d'Autremont is a doctor of medicine, not of philosophy. His father and his grandfather were both physicians, and it was assumed that he would become one too. He himself was not so sure. As an undergraduate at Princeton he was bored by physics and chemistry, and did poorly in both subjects, but liked the courses that he took in music and literature. For a time he thought he would like to be a writer. Then, in the summer before his senior year at college, he worked as an X-ray orderly in a hospital. This experience convinced him that a medical career had more to offer in the way of both intellectual and emotional rewards than he had suspected, and he made up his mind to get a medical degree. Because of his poor marks in physics and chemistry, however, it was not certain that this would be possible. He was turned down the first time around by every medical school to which he applied, and was accepted by Columbia's College of Physicians and Surgeons only after a number of wires had been pulled on his behalf by a doctor whom d'Autremont had met while working as a hospital orderly during the summer after his graduation from Princeton. His mentor's confidence in him proved well founded. When he graduated four years later he stood twenty-second in a class of over a hundred.

After getting his degree, d'Autremont spent two years as an intern and junior resident in pediatrics at Bellevue in New York, spent another two years as an Air Force medical officer in France, and then returned to New York as a senior resident at Babies' Hospital. By this time he had begun to wonder whether he really wanted to devote himself entirely to clinical medicine. He had gotten a taste of research at Princeton, where, instead of writing a term paper in a physiology course, he had spent many months trying to establish a link between the central nervous system of a salamander and its ability to grow a new tail. Although he had gotten nowhere at all with this investigation, he had found that doing research could be exciting in much the same way as writing stories or poems. Later, at medical school, he had struggled off and on for three years with a difficult and messy problem in microbiology. Again he had gotten nowhere. But unlike many people who try their hands at research, he had been exhilarated rather than depressed by the ambiguity and uncertainty that are inherent in experimental science, and had found that repeated failure did not generate any more anxiety than he could easily put up with. Thinking this over as the years went by, he came to the conclusion that instead of practicing pediatrics he would like to teach at a medical school and do research.

To do this he would need a solid grounding in research techniques. He applied to a well-known microbiologist on the staff of the Institute, and was taken on by him as a guest investigator, a position roughly equivalent to that of a postdoctoral fellow. The man in whose laboratory he now went to work had for years been interested mainly in streptococcal diseases, particularly in their relationship to rheumatic fever. D'Autremont spent three months in the Institute's library reading the relevant literature, and then began a series of experiments that he hoped would throw new light on the part played by viruses in the production of bacterial toxins in scarlet fever, a disease sometimes associated with rheumatic fever. This time he got some highly significant results. In 1962, when his two years as a guest investigator were up, he was invited to stay on as senior resident physician at the hospital that the Institute maintains for patients who are the subjects of clinical studies. This would leave him free to spend from half to two-thirds of his time in the laboratory, and d'Autremont took the job. In 1965 he was made an assistant professor and relieved of all responsibilities other than research.

D'Autremont finds it hard to imagine a better situation than he now enjoys. The cost of his research is paid for partly out of the Institute's income from endowments and partly out of federal grants that are applied for and administered by the head of his laboratory. D'Autremont himself has never had to write a research proposal of any kind. Such arrangements, which are fairly common in biomedical research, do not always work out so well for people in d'Autremont's position, who are sometimes treated like indentured servants by the older men on whom they are dependent for support. But although d'Autremont's chief follows his work closely, and is generous with advice when it is asked for, d'Autremont is free to study whatever he wants, in whatever way he wants to study it.

If he should be invited to stay on permanently at the Institute, he would be inclined to accept, even though in doing so he would be divorcing himself finally from clinical medicine. This is a prospect he can face without dismay only because he feels that as a researcher at the Institute he can still honor the physician's traditional commitment to healing. Although the work he does is basic, and although he enjoys solving scientific puzzles, d'Autremont's interest in streptococci, and in the mechanisms by which the body defends itself against them, is motivated less by detached curiosity than by the hope of doing something to lessen pain and suffering. "I have to fight hard to keep my feeling that I'm a physician who's interested in two or three diseases of man," he says. "This is not a popular thing here at the Institute. To be caught working on a disease is almost a cardinal sin." Many scientists at the Institute who study very much the same sort of things as d'Autremont studies tend to look down with aristocratic disdain at researchers who are even partly motivated by a vulgar desire to heal people or to keep them well. D'Autremont cannot conceive of doing research on any other terms.

The Department of Terrestrial Magnetism, a division of the privately endowed Carnegie Institution of Washington, has much in common with a nineteenth-century Utopian community. This is not to say that there is anything homespun or archaic about the research that is done there. Three of the thirteen permanent members of its staff have been elected to the National Academy of Sciences, and the Department's work in biophysics and radio astronomy, as well as its studies of the earth's electrical and magnetic fields, with which the Department was at one time exclusively occupied, are held in high regard by other scientists. But in a sense the scientists who work in the Department's laboratories on the outskirts of Washington, D.C., have renounced the contemporary scientific world. "The activities of the Department . . . in recent years," its former director, Merle Tuve, wrote in the Department's annual report for 1964–65, "may be characterized as a set of very specific research studies carried out with the clear intention of testing whether a highly personal and individual approach to research is still valid and effective in various areas of modern physics. . . ."

One of the principal elements of this approach is austerity. Although the Department's laboratories are excellently equipped, members of the staff are proud that they, and the twelve to fifteen visiting scientists and postdoctoral fellows who work with them, have all together only eight or ten research assistants and laboratory technicians. Furthermore, the Department applies only sparingly for government grants, preferring to get along on the three-quarters of a million dollars a year that is allotted to it by the Carnegie Institution. As a result the Department is scarcely any bigger now than it was fifteen years ago, and in the opinion of Ellis T. Bolton, a biophysicist who succeeded Tuve in 1966 as its director, staying small has decided advantages. "We are forced to exercise self-control," he told me. "Since we can't do everything, we think very carefully about what we should do. Even after we choose an area of investigation, we are constantly winnowing our ideas, working away with self-criticism of our own ideas. As a result, it's a very rare thing that a man has entered on what has turned out to be a fruitless venture." Another virtue of staying small, he said, is that "we don't have to dilute our time cooking up busywork for bands of technicians, or thinking up safe projects for other people to do."*

The Department's emphasis on personal research—in Tuve's view, "it somewhat incapacitates a research man if he can get a team to do his work for him"—is coupled with an emphasis on close cooperation. Individual research programs tend to be subordinated to a single group program. "Perhaps the best analogy is to a group of prospectors who explore for gold," Richard B. Roberts, the senior member of the Department's biophysics section, has written. "When one finds a rich lode, the others leave their exploratory work to help dig out the gold already located. As the lode is mined out, the separate exploratory ventures are resumed."[1]

At a university, a scientist's obligation to involve his

* Having to keep other people busy is one of the penalties of affluence. "Research assistants are a great danger to a young scientist," a professor of biology points out. "Research assistants have prestige value in your lab. If you have three or four, you are hot stuff. A fellow with a good project can get them. He has to keep them busy. So instead of doing inspired research, he thinks up things for them to do. I've seen many young scientists go downhill on this basis. They don't have time to do their research because of running the research assistants." [2]

graduate students in his own work may preclude his collaborating with other professors on a sustained piece of research. Members of the Department of Terrestrial Magnetism do not face this difficulty, and close collaboration with one another is also made easy by the fact that they depend so little on individual government grants for equipment or technical help, and can therefore afford better than most university professors to let years go by without publishing. "There's no pressure here to publish, except the responsibility a scientist has to communicate what he finds out," Bolton said. "We do ask each man to make a statement about what he's doing for our annual report, a kind of self-review. But in a small, intimate organization like this I don't need to weigh a man's publications to know how he's doing."

I gathered from Roberts that supplies, equipment, and laboratory technicians are as a rule communally shared by all the members of a particular research section. "It's important if we are to work together effectively that we operate out of a common fund," Roberts told me. "Here it's absolute communalism so far as equipment and chemicals are concerned. They're all over the place. You can operate that way when things are small and you respect one another's rights."

Probably not even the Department's most enthusiastic members would argue that all basic research can, or should, be done the way they do it. Cooperative research, no matter how democratically organized, is not everybody's dish of tea. "One postdoctoral fellow we wanted to keep on here turned us down because he wanted to play a lone hand," Roberts said. "He said, 'At this place, at the end of a year I can't tell what I did and what someone else did.'" Then, too, there is the kind of research that requires big machines and crews of technicians, and that is therefore incompatible with the Department's aims. "If you do this kind of science, then you're a manager, not a personal scientist," Tuve told me. "We are not part of this big new pattern of social research." He added that while he himself considers austerity an essential ingredient of creativeness, "plenty of scientists just love to have all the latest accoutrements." Some of these scientists, he admitted tolerantly, are very good ones.

Because there are a great many scientists who want to work with undergraduate and graduate students, universities are likely to remain the principal habitat even of those who want, in Tuve's terms, to be personal scientists. But the establishment of a few more research organizations patterned on the Department of Terrestrial Magnetism might have a healthy effect on the universities. They would offer such an attractive alternative to academic life that universities, and the government agencies that support their research programs, might be forced to find ways of easing the competitive pressures and lessening the distractions that scientists must now put up with if they want to teach as well as do research.

Oak Ridge National Laboratory in Oak Ridge, Tennessee, one of six so-called multi-program laboratories that the Atomic Energy Commission maintains, is in many ways the antithesis of the Department of Terrestrial Magnetism. With a $60-million annual budget, and nearly five thousand employes, most of whom work in a huge brick building that looks like a pharmaceutical factory, ORNL epitomizes "the big new pattern of social research" that Tuve and his associates reject. "[We] believe," Tuve wrote in one of his last reports as director of the Department, "that the primary purpose and the real and immediate use of basic research as we seek to carry it forward here lies in its effects on the spirit of man, shared by all men who value the contemplation of new knowledge in its firm relation to

the old."[3] By contrast, the aim of ORNL is to solve technological problems. At the time it was founded in 1943,
when it was designated simply as X–10, its mission was to
experiment with ways of producing plutonium for an
atomic bomb. Today ORNL has nothing to do with the
development of atomic weapons, but its assigned tasks are
still specific and practical. They include, among other
things, developing nuclear reactors that can economically
convert salt water into fresh, learning how to produce
power through controlled thermonuclear fusion, and finding ways to alleviate radiation disease.

But a good deal of basic research also goes on at Oak
Ridge. It is mainly of two kinds, examples of which were
given not long ago by ORNL's director, Alvin Weinberg.
"We have been working for many years at Oak Ridge on
the development of breeder reactors based on molten ura-
nium-bearing fluorides," he wrote. "To develop the breeder
we have had to keep many high-temperature chemists
busy over many years exploring the physical and chemical
properties of molten fluorides of the sort used in our reactors." He went on to say that "in addition to mission-
related work on molten fluorides, we have found it useful
to support much longer-range research on molten salt systems in general—studying their spectrophotometry, their
structure, their interactions with alkali metals. This kind of
research is 'more basic' than the former; it is more general
and often has wider relevance. Yet it has turned out much
of direct value . . . as well as creating a standard of scientific conduct for those engaged in the more applied work."[4]
Scientists at Oak Ridge do basic research in the biological
as well as the physical sciences; the laboratory's large biology
division, whose general mission is to study the effects of
radiation on living organisms, sponsors basic studies of, for
example, cell physiology and protein synthesis.

Each year there are people who leave Oak Ridge for

faculty jobs at universities and medical schools, and a
number of the younger scientists engaged in basic research
at ORNL think of it as a staging area in which to gird
themselves for an assault on the academic heartland. When
I visited Oak Ridge in 1965 I spoke with a member
of this group, a geneticist named *Kenneth Castle*. After
graduating from a small and undistinguished college,
which Castle told me he had picked mainly because he had
been offered an athletic scholarship there, he had gone as a
graduate student to a large and undistinguished state university. He got his Ph.D. there, but his thesis was too
weak to yield anything that could be published, and it was
clear that if he ever wanted to teach at a university he
would have to get further training in research. He got a
two-year postdoctoral fellowship at Oak Ridge, and when
he was offered a chance to stay on there after the two years
were up he took it—but not because he had given up his
hopes of becoming a professor. "The longer I stay here,
within limits, of course, the more opportunities there will
be for me at universities," he said. "I have a postdoctoral
fellow who works with me now, and I have a lab technician. Three or four nights a week I come back here to the
laboratory and work for several hours. I'm getting an awful
lot done. Of course, I miss having graduate students around.
There's an indefinable atmosphere of excitement at a university which I miss. But I have no responsibilities here
except to do research and publish it in professional journals,
and to write material for our semiannual reports. I'm proving
to myself that I can do research. Maybe not great research,
but very good. If I can't do it here, I can't do it anywhere."

Some older scientists with whom I spoke at Oak Ridge
had once had ambitions like Castle's, but had long since
dropped the idea of trying to go back to the academic
world. "I applied for a job here when I was finishing up as
a graduate student at Michigan," a physicist told me. "I

had a picture of Oak Ridge as a rather dismal place out in a sea of red mud. But when I came down for my interview I was rather favorably impressed. The people seemed very friendly, and when I was offered a job I accepted it. I didn't think I'd be here more than a year. I thought I would go back to the university and to teaching. But I found I could get quite a bit of satisfaction here, and for the most part I think I'm better off staying. Many universities are inclined to be much more competitive. I was lucky to fall into a good position here. I have a small research group, and we're free to design and carry out experiments as we see fit." He spoke for a few minutes about his work, and then returned to the subject of competition. "You have to make a place for yourself at a national laboratory just as you do at a university," he said. "But some universities are a lot more competitive."

But while one gets the impression that a good many of the liveliest and most talented people doing basic research at Oak Ridge would leave if they got an offer from a decent university, there are also scientists of first-rate ability who find its climate very much to their liking. Many of them are men who differ from scientists like Tuve and his associates in that they like, and have a knack for, organizing and managing big research groups. "The ecology of the research institute has a different tone [from the university]," Weinberg has said. "It is more hierarchical, its members react with one another more strongly, and it is interdisciplinary. In the individualistic, competitive university environment, genius flourishes but things go slowly because each genius works by himself with his own small group of students and assistants. In the less individualistic, cooperative institute environment, genius probably does not flourish as well, but things go very fast because so many different talents can be brought to bear on a given problem. It is a place in which, however, a single very able man can exert much more power and influence than he can in the university environment . . ."[5]

A widely respected biochemist whom I met at Oak Ridge, a man who would have no trouble at all getting a very good job on the faculty of a university or medical school, explained why he had found Oak Ridge an ideal place to work. After getting his Ph.D. in 1949, he said, he had spent four years in the biochemistry laboratory of a big hospital, where he was the principal research associate of a distinguished German-born scientist who had come to the United States as a refugee. He had then gone to a midwestern medical school as an associate professor of microbiology. "I rapidly became unenamored of teaching medical students," he said. "I had to teach pathology, microbiology—things I was not really interested in. I worked terribly hard preparing my lectures. But after years in which I had spent all my time in the most exciting kind of research, it was a letdown to look around the room and find half the class asleep."

In 1956 he went to Oak Ridge, where he had been invited to spend a year, and he has been there ever since. "They've provided me with everything I wanted," he said. "I started out working all by myself. Now I have a group that varies between twenty and thirty people in number, and an adequate budget. From the beginning I was able to bring in post-docs. I found good biochemists here, and I have been able to do very interesting work with people in other disciplines. I collaborated for quite a while with a maize geneticist who was interested in protein synthesis. For anyone who does sound work, and is productive, money is relatively easy to get here. At a university, over a period of years a man may have to write twenty different proposals. All I have to do is to write a five-page outline of my plans for the next few years. The young people in my group don't have to worry about money at all. The kick that many people get out of working with graduate students, I get from the postdoctorals. So far as I'm concerned, all this place lacks is the sophisticated cultural life of a big city."

VII

The Vineyards of Utility

T HE IDEA THAT science can be useful did not take root until the revolution in scientific thought that occurred in the seventeenth century, when Newton's universe replaced the universe of Aristotle. The leaders of this revolution believed that knowledge of the natural world was to be sought not only for its own sake, or for what it might reveal about the nature of God, but also for the material benefits it could confer on mankind. The new scientific societies that sprang up all over Europe in the 1600's were founded largely in the hope of realizing such benefits. Robert Hooke expressed this hope in a preamble he drafted for the statutes of Great Britain's Royal Society: "The business of the Royal Society is: To improve the knowledge of natural things, and all useful Arts, Manufactures, Mechanick practices, Engynes and Inventions by Experiment—(not meddling with Divinity, Metaphysics, Morals, Politics, Grammar, Rhetoric, or Logicks)."

For a time it seemed that science and technology, which up to then had run in separate channels, were at last converging. Newton's celestial mechanics led to improvements in the art of navigation, and Franklin's studies of electricity bore fruit in the lightning rod. In factory towns like Birmingham and Leeds, scientists, manufacturers, and engineers sought each other's company, and joined in car-

168

rying out scientific investigations and in launching new industrial projects. Watt's improvements on the old Newcomen steam engine owed something to his discussions with Joseph Black, the Scottish physician and chemist who first formulated the principle of latent heat. But they owed more to Watt's mechanical ingenuity, and for the most part the inventions that transformed manufacturing and transportation in the eighteenth and early nineteenth centuries were the work of mechanics who knew little or nothing of theoretical science.

Two things helped to bring about at last the marriage of science and the practical arts that Hooke had been so eager to promote. To begin with, there was an outpouring of scientific theories whose implications for technology could not be missed. No intelligent physician or food processor could ignore the germ theory of disease, as formulated by Pasteur and Koch. Nor did it require an exceptionally lively imagination to foresee at least some of the practical uses of electromagnetic induction. At the same time, businessmen and politicians found that it paid to mine science systematically for practical applications, and that men with formal scientific training made the best miners. Among the first to profit by this discovery were Germany's chemical manufacturers, whose commercial leadership was due in part to the fact that by the middle of the nineteenth century they had begun to build research laboratories and to staff them with graduates of Germany's excellent new polytechnical institutes.

The United States did very little in the way of chemical manufacturing before World War One, and American businessmen tended to have less respect for scholarship and science than their German counterparts. The first laboratories of applied research in the United States, with the exception of Thomas Edison's Menlo Park laboratory, were established by the Department of Agriculture, which was directed by the Hatch Act of 1887 "to promote scientific investigation respecting the principles and applications of agricultural science." In the early years of the twentieth century, however, a few companies, among them General Electric, Westinghouse, and Bell Telephone, established research laboratories of their own, and after the war hundreds of others followed their lead. By 1940, some 37,000 American scientists and engineers were employed in industrial research.[1]

But it is in the last twenty-five years that the number of people engaged in applied research has grown most spectacularly. In the nineteenth century, there was a lapse of fifty years between Faraday's demonstration that an electric current could be generated by moving a magnet near a piece of wire, and the construction, by Edison, of the first central power station. In World War Two, by contrast, only six years elapsed between the discovery of atomic fission and the detonation of the first atomic bomb. Radar and penicillin were developed in even less time. The lesson seemed clear: the interval between the discovery of scientific knowledge and its application could be greatly shortened if enough scientists—and enough money—were allocated to the task.

Politicians, generals, and businessmen were understandably impressed. The techniques of socialized invention that had been so effective in the war against Germany and Japan were soon being used in the cold war with Russia. Battalions of scientists and engineers were mobilized to develop the hydrogen bomb, the intercontinental ballistic missile, and other military systems and devices, and after 1957 more battalions were recruited for the task of matching Russia's feats in outer space. More and more people were also being employed to exploit science for other purposes. The development of penicillin had shown, for example, that big collaborative research efforts could be effective in medicine as well as in engineering, and groups of scientists were organized to take advantages of opportunities opened up by recent discoveries in biochemistry and immunology. Much of this research was paid for by the federal government, and by organizations like the National Foundation for Infantile Paralysis. But by the mid-1960's, American drug companies were spending nearly $300 million a year to develop new antibiotics and other useful (and profitable) drugs. Much larger sums are spent by companies in the chemical, electronics, and communications industries, whose profits, like the profits of pharmaceutical manufacturers, depend largely on the speed and imagination with which they make use of new scientific knowledge. Even in industries in which heavy investments in research may make little sense from a narrow economic point of view, businessmen have found that photographs of men in white coats gazing at a test tube—or, better yet, fiddling with the controls of a $50,000 nuclear-magnetic-resonant spectrometer—can help project an image of corporate dynamism.* By 1966 the number of scientists working in government or industrial laboratories, or employed by nonprofit organizations that do contract research for government and industry, like the Battelle Memorial Institute, had risen to more than 200,000. This total included roughly a third of all Americans with doctorates in one of the biological sciences, half of those with doctorates in physics, and two-thirds of those with doctorates in chemistry.[3]

The distinction between basic and applied research is

---

* In the bull market of 1960 and 1961, some companies sold stock to the public mainly on the strength of a scientific-sounding name. After losing money for four straight years, the Agricultural Equipment Corporation, a company whose main product was weed burners, changed its name to Thermodynamics, Inc. and offered the public 315,000 shares of its stock at $3.50 a share. The entire offering was snapped up, and within a week the stock was trading at $4.50.[2]

sometimes hard to draw. An astronomer who studies very distant celestial objects and makes inferences about the way the universe has evolved is plainly doing basic research. By contrast, a drug company chemist engaged in what has been called structural, or molecular, roulette, a game that consists of taking a compound with known pharmacological properties and tinkering with its molecular structure in the hope of turning up a compound with slightly different (and perhaps slightly better) properties, is just as plainly doing applied research. But it is not so easy to classify the work of an industrial researcher like James Cantelli, the physicist whose experimental work with lasers is described in Chapter II. In his choice of experiments Cantelli is guided by a desire to add to scientific knowledge in his field, and from his standpoint what he is doing is basic research. However, from the standpoint of his employers, who support this research because there seems to be a particularly good chance that it will yield technological dividends, his work might be classified as applied—or, more likely, as what has come to be known as "mission-oriented" research.

But however one defines basic and applied research, it is clear that scientists who pursue knowledge for its own sake are greatly outnumbered by those who pursue it for its utility. Most of the latter are in industrial research, which is the subject of the next chapter. The rest are to be found in university and government laboratories, and it is with their careers that this chapter is concerned.

Presidents of American universities sometimes give the impression that applied research, apart from what is done in their medical schools and from a few chores taken on at the urgent request of the government, is the kind of thing that goes on only at other institutions. In taking this line they are reflecting the views of members of their faculties of the arts and sciences, who tend to feel that professors, like priests or nobles, should not be concerned primarily with the merely useful. In fact, thirty-eight cents out of every dollar that universities budgeted for research and development in 1964 was for work that they themselves classified either as applied research or as development.[4]

Much of this work, to be sure, is done by people who are neither faculty members nor students. Many are employed at one of the roughly two dozen big laboratories and research centers that are wholly supported by government agencies, but that are under university management. These centers include, for example, the Los Alamos Scientific Laboratory, which does classified work on nuclear weapons for the Atomic Energy Commission, and which is managed by the University of California. When these laboratories were organized, faculty members were in many cases deeply involved in their direction. But in general their links to the universities that manage them are now purely fiscal and administrative, and they differ from government laboratories mainly in that their directors can hire, fire, and promote without paying attention to civil service rules. A lot of applied research also goes on at government-supported laboratories that are attached to universities and run by faculty members, but that are staffed mainly by nonfaculty researchers. These researchers have titles such as Senior Research Associate, or Principal Research Mathematician, and are sometimes referred to collectively as the Second Faculty. A second-faculty member is usually paid about as well as a professor of comparable experience and attainments. But in several other respects he is at a disadvantage. He does not have academic tenure. He cannot, as a rule, add to his salary by outside consulting. And, if he works in a laboratory that mainly does applied research, he can usually be switched from one project to another at the discretion of the laboratory director.

But in addition to the work that goes on at laboratories such as these, a good deal of applied research is done by individual professors, working either by themselves or with small groups of students, faculty colleagues, and research associates. A chemist who is an authority on a particular class of organic compounds may agree, for example, to synthesize certain compounds that the Army has reason to think may be effective against strains of malaria that resist standard antimalarial drugs. A professor may also take on a project because of its intrinsic scientific interest, because he gets a kick out of solving practical problems, because he can't get a grant for the basic research that he wants to do, or because he hasn't any ideas of his own that he is burning to pursue. "We have been quite successful in getting professors to do work for us," I was told by the associate director of a Navy laboratory that specializes in underwater communications. "The trick is to sort of sneak up on them. If we have a problem that we think a particular professor could solve, we invite him to come to the laboratory to give a seminar in his specialty. We may not happen to have anyone on the staff who will be able to really follow what he's talking about, but—let's say he's a physicist—we see to it that all the physicists come, and stay awake, and give him a big hand. Then we take him around to talk with some of our senior people about the work they're doing. If we work things right, he ends up volunteering to have a crack at the problem we had in mind for him all along." Often such encounters are ritualistic on both sides. Some professors look on research contracts as an end in themselves, and are ready to overlook the fact that a project is scientifically boring, and socially of questionable value, provided enough money is involved. As Gerard Piel, the publisher of *Scientific American*, has observed, "[The] university campus has come to harbor a new kind of *condottieri*, mercenaries of science and scholarship hooded with doctorates and ready for hire on studies done to contract specification."[5]

There is nothing intrinsically immoral, of course, about applying scientific knowledge and techniques to the solution of practical problems. This is what engineering mainly consists of, and members of engineering faculties spend a lot of time doing such things as investigating the properties of membranes in the hope of improving the performance of artificial kidneys, or trying to devise ways in which computers can be used to calculate the stresses on buildings and other large structures.* Some work of this sort is supported in the same way as basic research: that is, by grants or contracts that are awarded on the strength of a proposal made by a faculty member who intends to do the work himself. But there is not a great deal of money available on these terms for research in the engineering sciences, and even at a first-class engineering school a faculty member may take on research projects that bore him simply because there is no other way he can get a summer salary. "Our department has a very good reputation—everybody can get money," I was told by a young associate professor of civil engineering and engineering mechanics. "The question is whether you get it to do what you want to do. Fifty percent of the time I do what I want, fifty percent of the time I do stuff I don't like so well." Most of the work in the second category, he explained, consisted of solving

---

* Professors of engineering also do a lot of consulting. This serves several purposes. It keeps a man in touch with current practices and problems in industry; it permits him to test in practice the validity of techniques he has developed; and it may bring him in a good deal of money. A professor at a leading midwestern university, whose specialty is the application of modern mathematics to civil engineering, told me that he earns $40,000 a year, or just double his academic salary, from his work as a member of a firm of consulting engineers.

problems farmed out to him by older professors with large
Defense Department research contracts.

The discontent of this young engineer is only one symp-
tom of a malaise, sometimes referred to as an identity
crisis, that has afflicted the engineering professions in
America. Some engineers, both in and out of engineering
schools, are men of outstanding ability. They include, to
name just one example, Jerome D. Wiesner, an electrical
engineer who is now dean of science at M.I.T. and who
was President Kennedy's Special Assistant for Science and
Technology. Wiesner is respected not only for his skills as
a politician and organizer, but for his contributions to the
fields of communications theory and communications engineering, which were opened up by the work of, among
others, the mathematician Norbert Wiener. "Perhaps one
might put it that Wiener preached the gospel and Wiesner
organized the church," one of Wiesner's colleagues at
M.I.T. has said. "Jerry's real strength, I think, lies in his
ability to spot the potential importance of an idea long
before others do. He wants to assist in the realization of
the new physics. I don't know that I would call his a creative mind—he isn't likely to supply the things that are
missing. But give him a chance at the components that are
present, and you can bet on him to put them in place, so
keen is his organizing intelligence."[6]

But fewer men like Wiesner seem to be going into engineering today than thirty years ago, when Wiesner was a
graduate student. One reason is that scientists, by and
large, can now make just as good a living as engineers.
Another reason is that engineering lost some of its glamor
when the development of radar and the atom bomb
seemed to prove that scientists, if they would only put
their minds to it, could do anything that engineers could
do, and do it better. As Lawrence H. O'Neill, associate
dean of Columbia's School of Engineering and Applied

Science, pointed out not long ago, "most engineering schools are struggling to hold their student populations constant, and many have fallen behind." O'Neill went on to argue that this was because professors of engineering had become too much concerned with science and too little with engineering. "Despite the different purposes of engineering research and scientific research, the two are generally judged by the same standards," he wrote. "Thus the field of engineering is encouraged to imitate the style and flavor of the sciences; but since engineering is essentially tied to utility, this inevitably produces an alienation of engineering education from the profession it serves—and an 'also ran' feeling in the engineering professor."[7]

Few professors of engineering at Columbia, or at other leading universities, would agree with the remedy that O'Neill proposes—namely, that engineering schools should take on more large-scale development projects of the kind that are typical of most engineering work done outside the universities. But they would not quarrel with O'Neill's assertion that engineers have come to be regarded—and, in many instances, to regard themselves—as scientists *manqué*. This makes it hard for engineering faculties to recruit able new members. "People in this department have to feel comfortable in an engineering environment," I was told by the head of a department of chemical engineering that is considered one of the two or three best in the country. "Part of this is being willing to ask yourself constantly, 'What is the relevance of this?' You can't do things just for the pleasure it gives you. But that's not the only thing. There's the *idea* of being an engineer. A few weeks ago a young chemist we were interested in came here to visit. Before he left, I said to him, 'You might not be comfortable here.' I said, 'Ask yourself honestly if the title of assistant professor of engineering is something you feel you could live with.' He wrote later that he had thought carefully about what I had said, and that he had decided he would really rather stay in chemistry."

Since 1940 a new class of scientific institutions has flourished in the United States. It consists of laboratories like Los Alamos and Oak Ridge, where large numbers of scientists and engineers, working either directly or indirectly for the federal government, are engaged in such tasks as trying to develop better antimissile missiles, or better systems for controlling the flight of space vehicles. Some people at these laboratories spend part or all of their time, as I have indicated, doing basic research. But many more do applied research. Typically they work as members of teams, made up of specialists in several different disciplines, that have been given the job of clearing the way for the attainment of specified technological objectives.

To learn something about large-scale, socialized research of this kind, I spent a week at a big government laboratory, which I shall refer to as Midvale, and talked with a number of scientists who were doing (or managing) applied research in fields related in one way or another to atomic energy. I shall report briefly on what three of these men told me about themselves and their work. The first of the three is *Harold Sanderson*, a physicist whose work has mainly been related to the development of nuclear reactors, and to attempts to develop low-cost methods of taking the salt out of sea water. A cheerful, bubbling man in his middle thirties, Sanderson told me that he had begun to cultivate an interest in science at a very early age because he couldn't seem to do anything else well. "Science was a device by which I could get some measure of esteem and respect from my fellows," he said. "I wasn't very good at sports. I never learned to dance very well. Many people go into science as a refuge from an unsatisfactory social adjustment. I was one of them." He laughed, and added,

"Then, years later, you know, suddenly the timidity is gone. The lamb turns into a lion."

In Sanderson's case, this metamorphosis did not take place until he was past thirty. He grew up in Brooklyn, and after graduating from Brooklyn College he became a graduate student at Cornell. At first everything went well, but in his third year, when he settled down to work on his thesis, he ran into bad luck. "My adviser gave me what seemed like a good problem," he said. "What I was doing was a natural extension of some work that had just been published. But after I had been working away for eight or nine months, someone published a paper proving that there was a basic error in this work. In fact, the whole theory on which my thesis was to be based turned out to be erroneous." Like many government laboratories, Midvale offers summer jobs to graduate students, and after Sanderson's thesis had been shot out from under him he spent three months there. "It was a very pleasant summer," he said. "I was given some simple problems in nuclear physics—to collect some data and analyze it. It was the first successful working experience I had had." When he got back to Cornell in the fall he started on another thesis topic, but after wrestling with it for a year he came to the conclusion that the problem he had picked was insoluble. "I might have been able to grind out enough stuff to make an acceptable thesis," he said. "But I didn't want to pad it. I said to myself, 'Look, buddy, you've had it.' I had been offered a job at Midvale, and I decided to take it. There were lamentations from the family. I learned what it means in English novels when someone is sent down from Oxford. But I had a practical reason for leaving Cornell. I was married, and I was tired of living like a pauper on graduate student's pay. In those days we were only getting eighteen hundred dollars a year, and I was paying four hundred a year of this for tuition."

Government and industrial laboratories employ a good
many scientists who have started out to get a Ph.D., and
who have taken the required courses, but who have then
failed for one reason or another to produce a thesis. A
failure of this kind can be paralyzing, but Sanderson's confidence in himself was not permanently impaired. When he
got to Midvale he found he was having no trouble with the
problems in nuclear and reactor physics that he was given
to solve, or that he thought up for himself. "Almost right
away I began publishing papers and going to conferences,"
he said. "It wasn't long before I was even becoming something of an authority in my special field." At the end of
three years he put together a set of the papers he had
written, and sent them to a distinguished Cornell professor
who had at one time been associated with Midvale. "I
asked him if he thought I had enough there to make a
thesis," Sanderson said. "He wrote back and said that I had
made a fine beginning, and that he would be glad to take
me on as a doctoral candidate by mail. In about two years
I had my degree." Until then, Sanderson had been half
convinced that his failure in graduate school had been due
to stupidity rather than to hard luck, but this suspicion
was now dispelled. "From that point on the world was
my oyster," he said. "I got an offer to write a book on the
phase of nuclear physics I had been working on. I got a
little money from it, even a little fame."

Sanderson is the kind of physicist sometimes referred to
condescendingly as a "house theorist." His research consists mainly of working out the implications of well-known
physical laws in order to lay a foundation for the solution
of technological problems. He is unlikely to figure importantly in the history of man's attempts to grasp the nature
of physical reality. In the jargon of his trade, he is not
working at the frontier, and a career such as his would not
appeal to a young physicist who has been awarded a post-

doctoral fellowship at, say, the Institute for Advanced Study, and is dreaming of a professorship at Harvard or Berkeley.

Sanderson seems happy, however, in a job in which he places his ingenuity and professional skill at the service of people working toward practical ends. For nearly seven years the specific goal with which he was concerned was the improvement of nuclear reactors. Then, in 1961, he joined a group that had been formed to investigate techniques of desalination, and he began to do research in the physical chemistry of colloids. "It was a marvelous opportunity," he said. "I found the change infinitely refreshing. I was getting sick of the stuff I'd been working on all those years. I was able to work with two experimentalists in a marvelously fertile field." Like many scientists at Midvale, Sanderson occasionally teaches at a nearby university, lecturing to students of chemical and metallurgical engineering. He teaches mainly to earn some extra money, not because he is a frustrated academic. As a graduate student he had looked forward to becoming a professor, but by the time he had earned his Ph.D., and might have been able to get a regular teaching job at some university, he was no longer interested. "I didn't feel the same need I once did to bask in the admiration of students," he told me. "Besides, this is a great place to work. There isn't anything I might want to do that I can't do here. I could even migrate into biology." Sanderson said that he had recently shifted to a group that was studying certain aspects of civil defense, and that the move had confirmed him in his conviction that it was a good idea to change one's field every few years. "Your vision narrows," he said. "It's good to go into some field where you can offer fresh ideas. Of course, it may take six months or even a year to learn the tools of your new trade. Not everybody is willing to go to this trouble. Many people are content just to take their place in the army of ants laboring to build an anthill. I want to be at least a little bit of a trail blazer."

Richard Cox is a tall, handsome man with bright yellow hair, who could easily be mistaken, if it were not for his gentle and reflective manner, for a successful tennis pro. He grew up in a small New England city, where his father was a Congregational minister, and after graduating from Amherst in 1944 with a B.S. in physics he spent the next eighteen months at Oak Ridge working on the atom bomb. When the war ended he was not sure he really wanted to be a scientist. "I didn't feel I had been particularly creative at Oak Ridge," he said. "I thought of going into farming or into law. But I decided nothing was really going to be such a great improvement, and so I went to Princeton. My first boss at Oak Ridge was teaching there, and he had urged me to come and work with him." Cox got his Ph.D. in 1951, and went to the University of Pennsylvania as a research associate with the understanding that if things worked out he would be offered a faculty job in a year or two. Instead, he took a job at Midvale in 1953, and he has been there ever since.

Cox still seems saddened by a sense of loss and failure when he reflects on his departure from academic life. "I enjoyed my work at Pennsylvania very much," he said. "But to get to the forefront of physics, and to make contributions of long-range significance, you have to have a driving motivation, a burning curiosity. Really successful physicists care more about physics than anything else in the world. Even at graduate school I knew that wasn't the case with me. Still, I wanted an academic career. I was influenced in part, I suppose, by social value judgments. I come from a long line of ministers and teachers, and I was inclined to think highly of academic life. It had dignity. It was highly acceptable. It was the proper sort of thing for a chap to do. I told myself that maybe I would change, or that maybe I could make my way without having that passionate dedication to physics. But it didn't work. At Pennsylvania I was a competent and successful member of a team that carried out some quite good investigations. But I did nothing of individual note, and there was no point in my hanging around."

At Midvale Cox joined a group that was doing both fundamental and applied research. He hoped to divide his time between the two. But lacking real confidence in his ability to do anything important in basic research, he found it hard to resist the demands that were made on him in connection with the group's main task, which was to help develop safe and efficient nuclear reactors. "In applied physics you have to work on a timetable," Cox said. "Someone has to see that all the pieces somehow fit together. Soon I was asked to take on responsibility for the work of other people. I never got back to anything that people in the universities would accept as real physics."

Managing an applied-research program is quite different from running a university department. To explore the feasibility of a new technique for, say, controlling air traffic is likely to require the efforts of many people, and the effectiveness with which they do their jobs often depends heavily on the skill of their leader. Unlike a department chairman at a university, he must concern himself with more than budgets and housekeeping and recruiting. He must also decide how problems are to be tackled, and how they are to be divided up among the members of his group. He may even lay down the lines along which individual investigators proceed. Promotion to an administrative job may therefore bring with it more freedom and autonomy as well as more pay. "As an administrator you feel you have a bigger piece of the action," Cox said.

Cox is the head of a department that includes twenty-nine scientists and engineers. Some of them make measurements and computations intended to help engineers to design more efficient nuclear reactors. Others study the interactions between neutrons and various materials from which reactors are built. Three members of the group work on refining the basic theories of reactor physics; in Cox's words, their aim is "to clarify and extend our understanding of the physical phenomena going on in reactors, and to enable us to describe them more quantitatively." Another subgroup studies reactors of varying types to determine how well they are suited, economically as well as technically, for such different jobs as desalting sea water and driving merchant ships. "The traditional boundaries between science and technology are maybe not as clear-cut as they may once have been," Cox says. "This is simply because technology has become increasingly sophisticated. But, recognizing that, one can say that we're engaged more in technology than in science, in the sense that the objective here is to translate scientific knowledge into specific programs and projects. We regard our mission in large part as developing an energy source which will be useful to the world in many different ways."

Cox feels that the most important thing he does is to help the people in his department define problems clearly. Often, he said, he can do this even when the man he is helping knows a great deal more than he does about what is going on in his particular field of science or engineering. "Part of this relates to accumulated experience, and part of it just has to do with the give-and-take between two technical people," Cox explained. "The person doesn't feel that he's operating in a vacuum." Although he is a modest man, Cox is prepared to argue that people in jobs like his have a lot to do with success or failure in applied research. He resents any assumption that their work is purely mechanical, and he was offended by William H. Whyte's book, *The*

Organization Man. "I felt he was trying to make me out more of a cog in a machine than I really felt," Cox said. "Looking around at organizations that succeed, and organizations that fail, I'm constantly made aware of the role that individuals play, through their imagination, their diligence, insight, skill. They're not just interchangeable parts."

But to have seen the promised land of pure science and then to have been found unworthy to enter it can be a cruel disappointment. The gratifications that Cox's job affords doubtless seem meager at times in comparison with the rewards of scientific discovery. He appears to have little relish for the power that an administrator wields, and there are hints that he must sometimes struggle to convince himself that his work is not pointless—or that, even if it must be judged absurd from an existential standpoint, it is nevertheless somehow necessary and good. "There are times when you go home at night and say, 'What in the world did I do today?' " he said. "The first thing you say is, 'Well, I didn't do a durn thing myself.' But then you go back over it, and you say, 'Well, I guess maybe I helped so-and-so, and I got so-and-so straightened out—he was off on a wrong tack—and I got such-and-such a project lined up that will now go forward for quite a while without any further cranking.' Etcetera. Etcetera."

Some scientists give up respectable, if not brilliant, academic careers because they find being an administrator more exciting. Among these willing converts is an exuberant extrovert named *Gordon McAllister*. McAllister grew up in a small town in Texas, worked for three years after high school as secretary of his local chamber of commerce, spent four years in the Air Force during World War Two, and then went to a small university I shall call Southern Texas. His intention was to become a schoolteacher.

Instead, he got interested in biology, and on the strength
of an excellent academic record—he ranked third in a class
of more than twelve hundred—he got a graduate fellowship at Cal Tech. He got his Ph.D. there in 1952,
stayed on for a year of postdoctoral work, and then went
back to Southern Texas as an assistant professor. Southern
Texas was not a first-rate university, and since McAllister
had had offers from such universities as Yale, this was a
rather unorthodox step. But his adviser at Cal Tech had
urged him to take the job. "He was very persuasive," Mc-
Allister recalls. "He said, 'Gordon, you talk the language.
You understand Texans. Take the Texas job. Pull the place
up by the bootstraps. Bring it into modern science.' "

At Southern Texas, where he spent five years, McAllister
managed to be reasonably productive. Doing research
there was harder than he had expected it to be, however.
One difficulty was a lack of facilities. At Cal Tech he had
been studying the effect of light on plant growth, and he
had hoped to go on with this work. At Southern Texas
there were no greenhouses in which to grow the kind of
plants he had been using in his experiments. There were
no darkrooms or controlled light sources, and there was no
money with which to pay for any of these things. McAllister got around this by shifting to ecological studies, and
to studies of the biochemical processes by which light
affects plant growth—two lines of investigation that he
could follow without expensive facilities or equipment.
Another difficulty, one largely of his own making, was
harder to overcome. In his determination to pull Southern
Texas up by its bootstraps, McAllister complained loudly
about its shortcomings, and then cheerfully accepted appointments to faculty committees charged with looking
into his complaints. At the end of five years, he was a
member of fourteen committees. "I was chairman of most
of them," he recalled.

In 1958 McAllister moved to Washington to work for the Atomic Energy Commission in its division of biology and medicine. He had been hired to review research proposals submitted to one of the division's several branches, but he soon found himself doing many other things as well. He learned to prepare budgets and to defend them. ("It's a huckstering job, but I seemed to have a kind of flair for it," he says.) He also became active on several interagency committees. Within two years, he was chief of his branch, and within four years he was acting as deputy director of research for the whole division.

McAllister had planned to spend no more than two years in Washington, and then to go back to academic life. But when he finally left Washington in 1963 it was to become associate director of the biology division at Midvale. In Washington he had come to the conclusion that the way to get good results out of applied research is to mix it up so thoroughly with basic research that no one knows which is which. At Midvale, he said, he had been able to test out this idea. "Everybody here is doing basic research—he thinks," McAllister said. "But a lot of it is research that I can honestly say is mission-oriented. Integrating the two in the same damn place, that's how you get progress."

McAllister believes that progress in applied research, as in business, can be helped along by proper planning and organization. One of the first things he did at Midvale was to draw up a five-year plan. "When you have four hundred people in a division, including a hundred and sixty scientists, you're out of the horse-and-buggy stage," he said happily. "You're running a corporation. You need organization. I felt that by writing this document, and shoving it forward, I could cause the AEC to think where biology in the AEC is going."

The pleasure that McAllister gets out of being a scientific executive appears to be unmarred by even a trace of nostalgia for the life he gave up when he went to Washington. "In Washington I began to see I was a generalist rather than a specialist," he said. "You begin to see that you can take the diversified interests of many people and weld them into a program. Of course, they may not always be aware that they're being welded. You see how Joe Blow's program in Florida relates to so-and-so's program over in Rome, and you begin brainwashing him to go down the alley you want him to go—that's how you get programmatic research done. Another thing: I became aware that I'm really an interpreter. I can tell people like congressmen how all these wonderful things people are doing all tie in together. If I can do this better than research at the bench, which should I do? I made a deliberate choice to become an administrator. I know I'll never go back to the bench."

VIII

The Industrial Labyrinth

IN THE UNITED STATES, the marriage of science and the practical arts that Robert Hooke hoped the Royal Society would bring about has been consummated mainly in the laboratories of large corporations. The promoters of the union, to be sure, are not invariably happy with the results. "I feel we are in danger of being run down by our research and development," Charles Allen Thomas, chairman of the board of Monsanto, the third largest American chemical manufacturer, remarked dourly not long ago. Industrial research, he added, "is now stumbling in a plethora of projects, sinking in a sea of money, and is being built on a quicksand of changing objectives."[1] But while businessmen grumble about how hard it is to get their money's worth out of the scientists and engineers they hire, they hire more and more of them every year. In 1936, when Thomas became research director of Monsanto, the company employed only one hundred and fifty-three professional workers in its research and development laboratories. Twenty years later, the number had risen to more than 2,300. American corporations as a group have increased their outlays for research and development from less than one billion dollars in 1946 to more than six billion in 1965. In 1965 they also spent seven and a half billion dollars on research and development paid for by the federal government. More than half of all professional scientific workers in the United States are employed in private industry, including four out of every ten scientists with doctorates in physics, and six out of every ten with doctorates in chemistry.[2] The industrial laboratory, rather than the university, is now the principal habitat of the scientifically trained American.

As corporate research managers are at pains to point out when they recruit at universities, there are scientists in industry who are granted the same freedom to pursue their own interests, even if those interests lie in the domain of pure science, that they would have in academic life.*

There are several reasons why it may pay a company to employ scientists on these terms. They keep the management, and the company's engineers and applied scientists, in touch with what is going on in areas of basic science that are relevant to the company's business. They serve to demonstrate, by their scientific achievements, that their employers are progressive businessmen, alert to the opportunities for profit that may be opened up by advances in science, and at the same time cognizant of a responsibility to add something to the stock of scientific knowledge on which they draw. A company that has researchers on its payroll who are free to do pretty much whatever they like also finds it easier to attract able young scientists—most of whom it may hope that it can in time persuade to concen-

---

* Two sociologists employed by the Bell Telephone Laboratories have noted that industrial scientists who enjoy this freedom are really protégés, rather than employees, but that this can not be openly acknowledged because there is no place for protégés in corporate ideology. "One of the troubles with the protégé concept is that it violates contemporary notions of work," they write. "Protégés are doing something for which there is no recognized need, or they are fooling around for their own enjoyment. However, if one calls them professionals, these nasty features are suppressed."[3]

trate on solving practical problems. Finally, and most importantly, scientists in industrial laboratories who are permitted to tackle basic scientific problems of their own choice often end up making extremely valuable contributions to technology.

Sometimes these contributions are by-products. If a company hires enough researchers with the right kinds of scientific interests, they are bound to make discoveries from time to time that can be profitably exploited. But beyond this, companies hope that some of the scientists to whom they give a free hand in their research will choose to spend some of their time on problems whose solution will clear the way for the development of new products or the improvement of old ones. Despite the fact that many young scientists tend to look down on applied research as a scientific equivalent of going into trade, this hope is not unreasonable. To begin with, some scientists are really inventors rather than scholars. Their most important scientific work is the invention of techniques and instruments— the cyclotron and the bubble chamber are examples—that open up new avenues of investigation. In the right circumstances, such men may turn enthusiastically to inventing devices that are of practical rather than scientific value.

Furthermore, many scientists discover that they get a great deal of satisfaction out of doing work that has an immediate impact on the nonscientific world. Few men have the daring or the imagination to address themselves to the most fundamental scientific questions. Most scientists use established techniques to explore the ramifications and to test the limits of established theories, and a scientist who is doing research of this character in a field such as organic chemistry, where so many of the problems he might choose to work on have technological implications, may well decide that it would be perverse to choose those that are of purely scientific interest. It may take years to come to this conclusion. A chemist who has worked for a medium-sized chemical company for the past twenty years told me that he had taken a job there, soon after getting his Ph.D. at Columbia, because the company had offered to place at his disposal special equipment with which to do fundamental research in a field that he was already interested in. "I was able to go as deeply into this area as I knew how to," he said. "The company insisted that we apply for patents, but I didn't give a damn about them. All I was interested in was publishing papers." But over the years, he said, his attitude had changed. "Three years ago the company gave me a sabbatical. I spent a year at Wisconsin. I worked in a laboratory there with two young postdoctoral students. It was wonderfully stimulating, getting them to accept me as an equal, and in a sense recapturing that period of my life when I was a graduate student. I spent the year studying a puzzling anomaly I had run into in some work I had done here, but had never followed up. It was a good problem, and I had it about eighty percent complete when the year ended. But I haven't got around to finishing it. I realize that this is partly because the problem doesn't have the added feature of economic value. I still do fundamental research here at the company, and there's no reason why I can't go into anything just as deeply as I like. But I'm no longer really interested in problems that don't involve economic considerations. I've come to see economics as another variable to be dealt with in studying a reaction—there's pressure, there's temperature, and there's the dollar. I just don't have any desire to do research that is scientifically exciting but of no use to anybody."

Even a scientist who never develops an interest in practical applications may be drawn into fruitful collaborations with other scientists whose efforts to solve technological problems have raised interesting scientific questions. It was a collaboration of this kind that won the 1956 Nobel prize in physics for William Shockley, John Bardeen, and Walter Brattain, the three men chiefly responsible for the invention of the transistor. Shockley, a theorist with a strong interest in practical devices, had been convinced that materials of the kind known as semiconductors could be used for amplifying electric currents. When his first efforts failed, Bardeen, who had not shared Shockley's enthusiasm for inventing a new kind of amplifier, became interested in trying to understand Shockley's failure, which seemed inexplicable in the light of existing ideas about semiconductors. In the end, Bardeen proposed an entirely new theory to account for the behavior of electrons on the surface of solids, and this theory, which was confirmed experimentally by Brattain, led to the construction, in 1948, of the first solid-state amplifier, or transistor.

The transistor was invented at the Bell Telephone Laboratories, the research and development branch of the Bell Telephone System. Bell Laboratories employs more than 14,000 persons, and several hundred of these are scientists who are free to study whatever interests them, provided the area they propose to explore has some relevance to telecommunications.[4] They may work by themselves or in collaboration with one another, but as a rule they are not expected to be team players. Richard R. Nelson, an economist who has specialized in the study of the process of invention, has pointed out that while there was a certain kind of teamwork among the inventors of the transistor, this "did not mean a closely directed project with an assigned division of labor in the form of tasks and schedules for each of the team members. There were no closely defined goals shared by all members of the group. . . . The project was marked by flexibility—by the ability to shift directions and by the rather rapid focusing of attention by several people on problems and phenomena unearthed by others."[5]

Employees of the Bell Laboratories have made many important contributions to both science and technology besides the transistor. These include the coaxial cable; the concept of negative feedback, which made it possible to amplify telephone signals for long-distance transmission without seriously distorting them; and the mathematical theory of information, formulated by Claude Shannon, which led to major improvements in the coding, transmitting, and switching of messages. But despite the enormous benefits that American Telephone and Telegraph and certain other companies have gained by hiring good scientists and giving them their heads, the number of scientists in industry who are free to do what people at the Bell Laboratories refer to as "uninhibited research" is relatively small. Only a large company with a fairly stable business and good profit margins—or a regulated monopoly like A.T. & T., which can charge the cost of its research to its customers—can afford to invest large sums of money in undirected basic research. (Investing small sums is likely to be pointless; good scientists will seldom work where they will have no chance to talk with other people doing basic research in the same or in closely related areas.) And even a big company cannot reasonably hope to profit directly by investing in basic research unless, like R.C.A., Du Pont, or General Electric, it markets a wide variety of products—or a few products, like computers, embodying a great deal of advanced technology—that stand to be improved (or made obsolete) by advances in scientific knowledge. Finally, some businessmen whose companies might profit by investing in basic research just cannot stomach the idea of having people on the payroll who are permitted to do exactly what they like. For all these reasons, only a small fraction—perhaps one quarter—of the people who earn Ph.D.'s in the sciences and go to work in industry are destined to do the kind of work that scientists traditionally have done, and for which they have supposedly been trained. The rest become technical troubleshooters, members (or leaders) of groups engaged in the development of new products and processes, managers of research operations, or managers of operations such as production or the marketing of technical products.

When company recruiters interview a student who is finishing up at graduate school, they usually encourage him to talk about what he has been doing in the way of research and what he would like to do, and then set forth the advantages their companies can offer in the way of freedom, good facilities, and stimulating colleagues. A prospect is not asked to buy a pig in a poke, and before he is offered a job he is customarily invited to visit a company's research laboratories and size them up for himself. But because the demand for Ph.D.'s in industry is much greater than the supply, the prospect's visit is carefully stage-managed. His hosts see to it that he spends a lot of time with people who are doing basic work in his field, and is steered away from groups that are doing applied research of little scientific interest. Under the circumstances, he naturally tends to assume, if he is offered a job, that it will consist of working on his own as a basic researcher.

Sometimes, as in the case of a scientist named *Harry Mintoff*, who received a Ph.D. in physics at the University of Illinois in 1953, the assumption is correct. "I was in solid-state physics," he told me. "I chose this field because you could already at that time see the trend in experimental nuclear physics. It was getting to be all group activity, and having to schedule experiments on big machines. When I went to Illinois there was a friend of mine there, a fellow from my home town, and he was doing solid-state physics.

I could see these were the kind of experiments one man could get his arms around." Mintoff paused, and went on to say, "There was another thing. It was moderately clear that solid-state physics wasn't the forefront of physics. It wasn't the most fundamental kind of thing. But for that reason it wouldn't be so competitive. The best people at Illinois weren't going into it then—though they did later on. I hadn't scored very high on my qualifying examination, and maybe I was making an unconscious adjustment to being a reasonable-sized fish in a smaller pond."

In the early 1950's, most research in solid-state physics was being done in industrial laboratories. Although Mintoff would have been glad to get an offer of a teaching job at one of the two or three universities that were important centers of solid-state research, no such offers came, and he went to work for a leading electronics company. Unlike many young scientists, Mintoff had no great desire to continue working in the particular sector of his field in which he had done research for his thesis. "I said I was willing to do anything," he recalled. "They said, 'Bill Sandler here has some interesting problems in the field of low-temperature physics. Why don't you work with him?' I really knew nothing about the field—I had to start out reading up on it in the encyclopedia—and for a while I got my ideas from Sandler. He always had more than he knew what to do with. Then, gradually, he cut away and changed his field, and I have been on my own ever since."

Although Mintoff's research is basic, he spends a certain amount of time thinking about how it might be put to practical use. "Some of the best scientists here, men who are in an absolute sense the best, are also the quickest to find applications of their work," he said. "I don't happen to be very creative about applications, but I do have an obligation, in deciding what would be the best things for me to do in my research, to think in terms of the company's goals." Besides doing basic research, Mintoff also works from time to time on practical problems confronting people in other departments of the company. "Often what we do is to try to help someone understand why something works the way it does, so that they can figure out how to make it work better," he said. "Or someone may call up with a problem in plasma physics he thinks we can advise him on. There are other things, too, that people like me can do to help the company. Recently I went around from department to department to find out what needs they had that were in some way related to low-temperature physics. The idea was to see what those of us doing basic research in this field could do to be more useful to them, and still do good scientific work. This kind of thing not only helps me in picking research problems, but it makes it easier for me to spot developments in my field that are likely to affect the company's business—something that in a roundabout way might make one of our products obsolete, for instance."

When I talked with Mintoff, he had just come back from Zurich, where he had spent a sabbatical year at company expense. He said that while he had thoroughly enjoyed his stay there, he had no longing for an academic job. "If I were at a university I'd have a certain amount of worry about getting support," he said. "There's no problem here. And the time I spend on work having to do with practical applications is much less than I would have to spend on teaching and faculty committees at a university. I may not make quite as much money as I would as a top professor at some place like Columbia or Chicago. But a friend of mine who is at a university told me the other day that it might be worth taking a pay cut for the sake of the peace and quiet we have here."

Industrial scientists engaged in basic research are by no means all as well protected from commercial pressures as Mintoff is. He works for one of the few companies where large numbers of scientists have about as much freedom as the people who do "uninhibited research" at the Bell Laboratories. In many industrial laboratories, researchers must repeatedly drop what they are doing in order to take on such jobs as, say, figuring out why a certain chemical reaction that is part of a manufacturing process isn't taking place in the way the company's process engineers anticipated. Such troubleshooting seldom has much to do with what a scientist is doing in his laboratory, and it is almost invariably regarded as an irritating distraction. Some companies therefore refrain from asking scientists engaged in basic research to do this sort of work. A scientist may be expected, however, to give a certain amount of time to the development of new products that grow out of his own research. This can be resented just as much as troubleshooting. "Organic chemists get involved in the problems they work on," a chemist points out. "The *chemical* problems can become quite important to them, and when the problems are difficult the chemist will be quite frustrated and tense. Then to have his work broken into . . . can be the cause of a good deal of frustration and resentment. It's not a good idea to take people away from problems in which they are engrossed."[6]

In deference to such attitudes, a company may leave it up to each individual researcher to decide how much or how little he will be involved in the development of new products. But this is a little like abolishing taxes in favor of voluntary contributions. Speaking of development work, an industrial scientist says, "Now I don't mind doing it once in a while . . . if it's for the good of the company, but I want to keep working on my own things too. I cannot be like some others. The way they do exploratory work is by refusing assignments if someone asks them for help. If someone asks me for help, I will give it to them, I have to, I cannot refuse it. If everyone here would act the way they do, there would be no Central Research Laboratory at all. The company would take a look and say, 'What are these people doing? They're refusing to help us!' "[7]

Fortunately for people who feel this way, there are scientists in industry who like to do a fair amount of developmental work if it is tied in closely with their research. A researcher who was spending roughly half his time studying the properties of glasses and ceramics, and the other half tinkering with the composition of particular glass and ceramic materials that seemed to have commercial possibilities, told me that he finds the combination a very happy one. "Some people are best suited to short-range, applied work," he said. "Some people are only interested in long-range work. I like being in the middle. When you go into industrial research, you decide that you're going to serve the company's interests, and doing this short-range work gives me a better feel for the kind of long-range research I should be doing. Also, it's really quite satisfying to see a product come out that you've done the fundamental work on."

Because the brightest graduate students tend to go into academic careers, the competition that a young scientist confronts in industry is less formidable than the competition he would have to face at a major university. But in industry, as in academic life, freedom to work on whatever one wants to is contingent on having good ideas and demonstrating the ability to carry them out. In laboratories that support a lot of basic research, a recruit just out of graduate school may be given a couple of years in which to show what he can do on his own. If he is clever or lucky enough to hit on something that seems likely to make money for his employers, he can usually count on being given a free hand from then on. If he has no flair for invention, he must establish his right to independence by publishing papers that attract the attention of other scientists. This not only shows that he is qualified to serve as an ambassador to the world of pure science, but enhances his bargaining power vis-à-vis his superiors by making it clear that he can easily get another job if he feels he is being pushed around. Simon Marcson, a sociologist who studied a large industrial laboratory in the late 1950's, quotes a supervisor who told him, "In the case of some individuals, I would not dare to shift them or to direct or even supervise them. They are the people who are very good. They know what they are doing. They know how to do it. They can be and are left completely on their own."[8]

Many scientists who fail to win the kind of autonomy that a man like Mintoff enjoys become problem solvers. They are assigned to groups engaged in what may be described as exploratory development. Such groups are not expected to explore unknown scientific territory; they are charged, rather, with finding the best route across scientific terrain whose main features are well known but have not yet been accurately mapped. Most of this work is done by engineers, and by scientists who have only bachelor's or master's degrees, who together constitute the great majority of all professional workers in industrial research and development. But a fair number of scientists with Ph.D.'s are also involved, not only as leaders of groups but as members of the rank and file. Some become part of the proletariat of industrial research, carrying out routine tasks under fairly close supervision. Others assume a role more like that of professional consultants. Often these are men who have gone through graduate school without having convinced either their professors or themselves that they have what it takes to do research on their own. They have learned how to use certain conceptual and experimental tools, but are at a loss to know what to use them for. As a result, they are often happy to settle for a job in which they will be called on, like doctors or lawyers, to use their professional skills to solve problems brought to them by other people.

Most problem solvers correspond to general practitioners in medicine. Their stock-in-trade is versatility rather than specialized expertise. Others are specialists in a particular technique—X-ray crystallography, for example, or the application of statistical theory to experimental design —whose skills are available to anyone with a problem in their field of competence. A specialist may attend scientific meetings, and even publish a paper now and then. But as a rule, the problem solvers, like the proletarians, withdraw from the Great World of science to which they briefly belonged as students. They find their rewards in the approval of their immediate associates and their superiors, and in the raises that an industrial researcher with a Ph.D. can count on if he is reasonably hard-working and resourceful, until his salary, after fifteen years or so, reaches a ceiling of perhaps eighteen to twenty thousand dollars a year.

At least a third of all scientists with doctoral degrees who go to work in industry end up as managers. Some of these leave research entirely. In many companies, the central research laboratories are used as a recruiting ground by other divisions, and some students now look on a doctorate in chemistry or physics as the equivalent of a degree from a graduate school of business administration; they go into industrial research with the hope of being able after a couple of years to move into a good management job in production or sales. But most scientists who become managers graduate from doing research themselves to directing the research of others.

Research administration exposes a scientist to new and often painful pressures. At the lowest level of laboratory management, it is true, the administrator's position is not altogether unlike that of a professor who has ten or twelve graduate and postdoctoral students in his laboratory. Like the professor, the leader of a research group in industry suggests research problems and ways of going about solving them to the people working under his direction. In many cases he may also try to help them develop their scientific competence. But the resemblance stops there. The professor decides for himself what research he wants to do, and he has a tacit agreement with his students providing that if they help him with this research he will train them to do research on their own. By contrast, the leader of an industrial research group is not so free to set its goals. Very often members of his group would like to work on fundamental scientific problems that may take years to solve and whose solution may be of no foreseeable importance from a technological point of view. But the group leader is under pressure from his superiors to persuade his people to work on projects that can be carried through quickly and that will pay off commercially. The nature of this conflict has been well described by a former president of the American Society for Public Administration, Harvey Sherman. The typical corporate executive, Sherman observed not long ago, sees the scientist as "a narrow specialist with no interest in efficiency or economy or in the overall objectives of the enterprise, a person who . . . objects to all types of control, and who is more interested in impressing other members of his profession than in the success of the enterprise for which he works." Sherman noted that the scientist takes an equally dim view of the executive: "By and large, the scientist sees [him] as a bureaucrat, paper shuffler, and parasite; an uncreative and unoriginal hack who serves as an obstacle in the way of creative people trying to do a job, and a person more interested in dollars and power than in knowledge and innovation."[9]

Under the circumstances, the lot of the research administrator is not an altogether happy one. His situation has been discussed at length by, among other people, a General Electric staff specialist named Lowell Steele. Writing in *International Science and Technology*, Steele has pointed out that the conscientious research manager "is continually effecting delicate compromises." When he has to take on an assignment that is lacking in scientific interest, he must persuade the people whom he asks to do the work that the company will make it up to them—by raising their salaries, for instance, or by giving them more opportunity in the future to do work that they are interested in. But this is a tricky business because, as Steele observes, "the manager has only limited influence over the sponsoring organization [and] he is in danger of promising his people too much."[10] The research manager must also put a great deal of effort into trying to persuade his superiors that the kind of long-range, scientifically significant work that the people in his group are eager to do will eventually yield big technological dividends. This has its dangers too. As another student of industrial research, Herbert Shepard, observed some years ago in a lecture at the Centre D'Etudes Industrielles in Geneva, "while the research director might like to think in terms of a five-year project which really cannot be evaluated in the first four years, he is likely to find that such a prospect reduces top management to a state of nervous exhaustion. This in turn reduces the research director to a state of nervous exhaustion."

A research administrator as a rule can be a scientist only by proxy. This makes some administrators very uncomfortable. A chemist who works for a chemical manufacturing firm told me that he had started out in fundamental research and had then gone up through the administrative ranks until, after twelve years, he was put in charge of all exploratory research. "I was involved in coordinating, organizing, keeping people happy," he said. "I myself wasn't very happy in this situation. I didn't have any control over what was going on. I felt left out in the cold. I was completely dependent on my secretary, and on the people working in the different laboratories. I found this a very unpleasant kind of existence. I would go into a laboratory, and I would be envious of the people working there. They couldn't understand it. The majority of people who get Ph.D.'s in chemistry—the majority of the ones we get here, anyway—*hate* to work in a laboratory. Their way out is to take a job in administration. But I didn't go to graduate school to be an administrator. When the company put in a scientific ladder so that senior people could do research and not have to become managers in order to earn a decent salary, I went back to research. I've been happy ever since."

It is not always easy to go back. The chemist I have just quoted had contributed so importantly to his company's profits, both as a researcher and as a manager, that he was in a position to write his own ticket. But a scientist who becomes a manager and does a poor job—or simply has bad luck—may find that he has become a man without a profession. He may have a hard time getting a job either as a manager or a researcher. "Suppose I was a director of research and for some reason or other they fired me," a young physicist remarks. "Where could I go to find another job as director of research? I have seen two candidates come in as job applicants the last year, who have been directors of research and at this point were willing to go back to the bench, but no one would hire them. As a scientist with papers to my credit, I can get a job anywhere. I have security. Furthermore, I know what I am contributing as a scientist; I know what I am doing for science and for humanity. But as a research director it becomes much more nebulous. What am I contributing?" He adds, "Also, as a scientist with publications and patents I have quite a bit of power within my own group to decide what to do. But what power do I have as an administrator in a middle management position? I don't think very much, at the present. I think a lot of these fellows have started to climb up on the managerial side and are not really thinking through what it would feel like when they got up there."[11]

Some scientists in industry find administration very much to their liking. Often they are men whose enthusiasm for doing research has been tempered, not long after they got out of graduate school, by an awareness that at best their contributions to science are likely to be very modest. In these circumstances a scientist may conclude realistically that if he wants to get ahead he must identify himself with his company, rather than with his peers in the world of pure science. Observing that the company sets great store by scientists who not only make the company's goals their own goals, but who are good at persuading other scientists to do likewise, he begins to drift into administration.

This evolution may be illustrated by the career of a physicist named *Donald Hurley*. Hurley grew up in Pittsfield, Massachusetts, where he graduated from high school in 1944. He spent two years in the Army, and then went to Union College in Schenectady, New York, under the G.I. Bill of Rights. His intention was to become an engineer and perhaps to get a job at the General Electric plant in Pittsfield where his father had worked as a machinist for many years. In his sophomore year, however, Hurley decided he was more interested in science than in engineering, and after graduating from Union he went to the University of Wisconsin as a graduate student in physics. He got a master's degree, but flunked the qualifying examination for doctoral candidates, and dropped out of school. He worked for a year as an electrical engineer, and then went back to Wisconsin. This time he squeaked by his qualifying examination, and went on to get his Ph.D. in 1957.

"I originally thought I wanted to teach," Hurley told me. "My profs at Union seemed to lead a very satisfying life. But my professor at Wisconsin got me enthused about research. Still, I had doubts about whether I could do research by myself. At Wisconsin, it was my professor who had the ideas. I couldn't honestly lay claim to having had a single original idea of my own." Hurley had one offer of a teaching job, but it was at a southern university, and he and his wife did not want to live in the South. He had also been invited to visit several industrial laboratories, including the central research laboratory of a company I shall call Northeast Products, which is located in a small Pennsylvania city. "This was the last place we visited," Hurley said. "My wife and I knocked around the town for two or three days. The other laboratories had been in places like Boston or Rochester, and we didn't want to live there. We're basically small-town people, and we liked it here. People here are hospitable. We decided to stay."

Northeast had just decided to do more research in solid-state physics, and Hurley, whose thesis work had been in the field of magnetic resonance, was asked to set up a magnetic-resonance laboratory. "I wasn't worried about the nuts-and-bolts aspect of setting up a lab here," Hurley said. "At Wisconsin I made three false starts before I finally got a thesis—that's why it took me so long to get through—and I had had plenty of opportunity to get familiar with the techniques and equipment. The company gave me plenty of time and plenty of resources. It was making a deliberate attempt to build up its basic physics, in the hope of opening up some area that would be technologically important. They had decided to do something in magnetic resonance because of what it might contribute to understanding the structure of glass, which is very important to this company. I spent the first year just diddling around. Then I found a couple of problems I could concentrate on. But it was nearly three years before I got into anything meaningful from a technological standpoint."

The work Hurley was doing was of some scientific interest, and he did publish one paper during his first three years at Northeast. But he said he had found it more exciting to look for new data that might prove useful to the company than to analyze and write up old data for publication. "Anyway, I got enmeshed with other guys here, doing other things," he explained. "I liked it here, and I wanted the company to grow and to get better. I spent a lot of time trying to persuade people to come to work here in the laboratories. I just was not terribly concerned about publication. I got my satisfaction out of our own internal growth and development here at Northeast. Unlike a lot of people, I never talked about this as my first job. Right from the beginning I thought of it as a long-term business."

After a time two technicians were assigned to Hurley, and a little later the company hired two young physicists just out of graduate school to work with him. "But I didn't consider myself as a manager," he said. "I regarded these two fellows as my colleagues. I assumed I would go right on doing work on magnetic resonance, studying the optical properties of solids." Then in 1963 a separate department of solid-state physics organized, and Hurley was appointed as department manager. He was authorized to add more physicists to his group—by the end of 1966 there were six in all, including Hurley—and to extend the work they had been doing to include studies of semiconductors and of other materials as well as glass.

"For the first couple of years I was nearly as active in the laboratory as I had been before," Hurley said. "But I was getting more and more involved in the overall operations of the organization. I went around and made a lot of noise about getting a better machine shop, for instance. I was also deeply involved with the technical problems of each of the guys who was reporting to me, and gradually I stopped doing research myself and became a manager. I've stopped regarding these guys as colleagues. I look at them as subordinates. The difference is that from time to time I have to look at them with a jaundiced eye and evaluate their performance."

Hurley sees his main job as helping the scientists in his department to find ways of doing what he is convinced they really want to do—that is, to help the company. "The basic direction of a research department is set when you hire people," he said. "You hire a man because you know he's interested in the things you want to have solved. Still, I spend a lot of time thinking how I can get guys to work in those particular areas in their field of interest where the company has the best chance of getting a return on its investment. This can be difficult. You don't push people around. After they've been here a while, you don't have to. When guys get out of graduate school they've been subjected for years to the mystique of research. But, by nature, a lot of guys who get through graduate school as experimental physicists are really inventors; they're gadgeteers and inventors at heart. After a while they find that it's not really disreputable to be inventing something useful. And there's a certain amount of pressure generated every month when you get your check. The company pays physicists well to do what they like doing, and you feel it would be awfully nice if you could do something for the company in return. I can relieve my guys of some of this worry because I'm in a position to see which of the things they might do are the ones that are likely to be most important to the company. Sometimes I have to try to get people to stop things. Some guys keep whaling away at a project.

They want to fill in all the holes, even though it's gotten to a point where it doesn't really interest anyone else any more. Still, it's my feeling that a good manager won't try too hard to squash a man who insists on doing something that doesn't happen to seem very relevant. If a guy has enough conviction, you damn well ought to go with him."

Not all research managers have drifted contentedly into their jobs as Hurley has. A scientist whose work in the laboratory has been highly productive, and who would on the whole rather do research himself than boss other researchers, may take a job in management when one is offered to him because it seems the lesser of two evils. This happens often in laboratories where a man who has done a good job as a researcher is regarded as having an obligation, both to himself and to his company, to take on managerial responsibilities. In a book called *Managers and Scientists*, two Harvard Business School professors, Ralph M. Hower and Charles D. Orth III, report that this view was almost universally shared by the managers of a number of industrial laboratories that they visited in the mid-1950's. "Sometimes explicit and almost blatant, sometimes unstated but clear enough in the way scientific personnel were being appraised, the message was plain," they write. "A good man should be promoted to managerial positions; a scientist who rejects an opportunity for such advancement will be held down in status and pay. . . . Indeed, it appeared to us in some instances that men who insisted on staying in research were subject to treatment which in effect constituted punishment."[12]

Many companies, conceding in principle that an able and energetic scientist who wants to stay in research may be worth more to his employers if he is encouraged to do so, have set up what is called a scientific, or technical, salary ladder. A scientist who reaches the top rung may earn more than all but two or three of his company's re-search managers. This is fine for a researcher who doesn't care whether or how his work is put to practical use, and who wants only to be left alone to do experiments and to publish the results.

But a scientist who wants to invent things and see them used may feel differently. Unless he knows his company's plans and has some chance to help shape those plans, the chances are slight that practical applications of his work will be made. He may therefore choose to go into administration because he realizes that a job on the scientific ladder will remove him from the main arena of organizational struggle and lessen his opportunities for influencing the people who control his company's affairs. His opportunities in such a position will be further lessened if, as is often the case, the belief prevails that the real measure of a man's worth, when one comes right down to it, is his ability to manage other men. As a result, jobs on the upper rungs of the scientific ladder, which may carry titles such as Senior Scientist or Scientific Adviser, are often regarded as consolation prizes for men who are obviously unfit to be managers, or who have been given a crack at managing and have failed to cut the mustard.

Another reason why scientists often shun the scientific ladder is that getting to the top can take an awfully long time. When the director of a laboratory retires, or is promoted, his job has to be filled, and so does the job of the man who is picked to fill it. When a Senior Scientist retires, however, years may pass before anyone is appointed to take his place. Moreover, while a scientist who chooses the scientific ladder may eventually earn $30,000 a year or more, he cuts himself off from certain opportunities that remain open to those of his associates who choose administrative careers. As Herbert Shepard points out, "The research scientist or engineer may well aspire to a position in top management if he begins to move up the managerial ladder; but a step up the technical ladder is towards a point of no future and no return."[13]

Many of the reasons that push ambitious young scientists into management are set forth by a physicist whose remarks are quoted in a case study used by students at the Harvard Business School. The physicist, to whom the authors of the study give the name of Milton Berger, begins by observing that the scientific ladder in his company "is really a sort of fiction and a pigeonhole." What he really wants, Berger says, is not to sit off by himself, but to have "a slightly larger group and a lot more freedom to decide what to do." He adds that he would like to have a voice in formulating laboratory policy, and then explains why it is important to him to be well paid for his work: "I like prestige and recognition as well as anybody else. If I make a contribution as a scientist, I should get recognition, and I should get higher pay. . . . I am giving up something by working here; I had a possible career in the academic world, so I want either money or a certain degree of fame. If I contribute in industry, it means that my scientific fame will be lower and that I will be less able to make scientific contributions. If I make this compromise with my scientific goals, I want to be paid for it." Berger goes on to speak of the way in which money, prestige, power, and freedom are related in an industrial laboratory: "The company prestige and the money actually go hand in hand, and I want prestige to get the freedom and the power to protect myself, to pick projects that I want to do. . . . I should be involved in discussions of the company and company policy; I should be learning about what the company is and how it operates so that I can know the company and do the job of proposing areas for future research the company should be in. It is meaningless to call me in the office and say to me: 'Think about areas of research that the company should be in,' without giving me sufficient background."[14] Berger's aims are widely shared by able and energetic young scientists in industry, and can usually be attained only by going into management.

Executives of companies like Monsanto, whose profits depend so heavily on the resourcefulness of the engineers and scientists in their employ, are not alone in their conviction that appalling amounts of both talent and money are wasted in industrial research and development. A great many industrial researchers hold the same view. In the late 1950's, thirty-five hundred scientists and engineers, employed by twenty-three different companies, were asked this question: "Is the research division [of your company] well organized for effective research?" Half of the people polled answered No.[15] The view that industrial research is inefficient would seem to be borne out, at least so far as big companies are concerned—and most scientists and engineers in industrial research and development work for big companies—by the investigations of a Purdue professor named Arnold Cooper. On the basis of interviews with managers who had been responsible for developing new products for both large and small companies, Cooper concluded that a large company is likely to spend three to ten times as much money to develop a particular new product as a small one would.*[16]

One important reason why industrial research is often inefficient is that, as I have indicated, the brightest young

---

* In one instance given by Cooper, a big company set out to duplicate a new protective coating compound that had been put on the market by a small competitor. The small company had a research department consisting of two chemists, one of whom had developed the new product by working on it part-time for twelve months. The total cost of the project was estimated at $1,400. The big company, whose protective-coating division had a development laboratory staffed by fifty chemists and technicians, spent eighteen months and $11,000 to do the same job.

scientists seldom want to work in industry. Their reluctance is due in part to the fact that the values and folkways of businessmen are so often incompatible with the values and folkways of scientists. Most corporate managers can see no reason why a scientist should object to working on those projects that his employers have decided are the most likely to pay off commercially. And many scientists do not object, provided they are not kept on too short a tether. But other scientists resent any curb on their freedom to investigate whatever they like. In the past, when academic salaries were poor and there were no government grants to pay for instruments, supplies, and summer salaries, an able scientist could sometimes be persuaded to pass up the independence of academic life in order to enjoy the benefits that industry offered—a decent salary, a well-equipped laboratory, and a chance to spend all his time on research. Today there are still scientists who resign from university faculties to take jobs in industry. But many more leave industrial jobs to become professors.[17] Moreover, many of the ablest young scientists who go into industry do so with the idea of establishing a reputation that will allow them to shift to a university later on. This can be done only in a job that permits a scientist to do research of a rather basic character, and unless a company is known to support such research it stands little chance of attracting first-rate people. Even managers of laboratories where a lot of basic research is carried out complain that it has been getting harder and harder to hire really good young scientists. Some are inclined to blame this on the fact that graduate students have become lazy and spoiled. A more likely explanation is simply that the number of energetic and talented young scientists has not been increasing so rapidly during the past ten years or so as the number of good academic jobs. "We don't get the real good guys," I was told by a chemist who does a lot of recruiting for his company, a petrochemical firm that employs some forty Ph.D.'s in its central research laboratory. "The kind we talk to are the kind we don't want—the guys who are just getting by."

Besides their fear of being too narrowly restricted in their choice of research problems, there is another closely related reason why talented young scientists tend to shy away from industry. Even though big corporations customarily plan five, ten, or even fifteen years ahead, few are willing to put much money into the kind of research that will pay off, if it pays off at all, only after many years. According to Nelson, it cost the Bell Telephone Laboratories around $200,000 a year to support the research on semiconductors that Shockley and his associates were doing in the late 1940's. "This is high-priced talent at work," he notes, "and when the project was initiated no guarantees were given as to the profits which would result. And for about two years before the transistor was invented, the group was kept free from pressure to produce practical results. This is not the type of project a small industrial laboratory is likely to be able to afford."[18]

Even in big laboratories, the management often takes a dim view of long-range, speculative research, and puts strong pressure on scientists to spend their time on projects whose outcome is fairly sure to be favorable, and that can be carried out in a few months or, at most, a year or two. A recruit who yields to this pressure and becomes a professional problem solver may be quite content for a number of years. The problems he gets are sometimes interesting, and almost always manageable. By taking them cheerfully as they come, he not only assures himself of regular raises in pay, but avoids the emotional and intellectual perils that would beset him if he were to try striking off on his own into unknown scientific territory.

But the problem solver faces the danger of early obsolescence. If he is a generalist, a sort of scientific handyman, the problems he deals with will often lie outside his special field of competence. In any case, they will seldom be related to the problems that people who are doing basic research in his field are grappling with. As a result, he tends to get out of touch with what these people are doing, and in time he discovers that there are many problems that he is less qualified to handle than men ten or fifteen years his junior, who are just out of graduate school, and who know how to use experimental methods and apply concepts with which he is unfamiliar. The problem solver who specializes in the use of a particular instrument or technique faces a similar danger. Even if he has kept up with what other people who use the same technique are doing, the technique itself may become obsolete.

Keeping up-to-date and holding on to one's ability to respond to and assimilate new ideas is a serious problem for all scientists in industry. The industrial scientist does not continually have to examine his own ideas, and to consider the relevance of his research to the major problems of his discipline, in the way that a professor who is conscientious about his teaching is forced to do. Nor does he have graduate and postdoctoral students in his laboratory who can teach him new techniques—and, more importantly, challenge him to defend his ways of thinking. Furthermore, if a scientist is doing classified research, or research whose results have to be kept confidential for competitive reasons, he is deprived of some of the intellectual nourishment scientists get by talking with other people in their fields. He can go to scientific meetings and listen to other people discuss their work, but it is hard for him to take part in a fruitful exchange of ideas when he is forced to keep many of his own ideas under his hat. "I go to one of the Gordon conferences every summer," an industrial chemist told me. "You can always tell the people from industry. They just sit and take notes, and practically never open their mouths. You don't talk to your competitors about business, even if they're old personal friends. You publish *after* a patent is granted. Until then, you don't say a word."

Professors as well as industrial scientists run the risk of becoming intellectually sterile at an early age. The danger is especially great for those who, like specialized problem solvers in industry, earn their keep by systematically mining a narrow vein of knowledge to which they have staked an exclusive claim—and which may suddenly peter out. When this happens, an academic scientist may lack the energy to begin prospecting for a new lode. But he is in a better position to prospect than if he were in industry. Assuming he has academic tenure, he can afford to risk two or three unproductive years while he feels his way into a new field. And, as I have suggested, the chances of being able to switch fields successfully are better for scientists who have been compelled, as teachers, to retain a certain breadth and flexibility that specialists in industry are apt to lose. Moreover, there are other things besides research that an academic scientist can turn to if he finds himself out of the research game. He can do more teaching. He can interest himself in curricular reform. He can take on a heavier share of departmental chores and committee assignments, and thereby relieve the pressure on his more productive colleagues. He can write textbooks. He can become a department head or a dean.

Many scientists in industry comfort themselves with the thought that if worse comes to worst they can become administrators. A scientist who was interviewed by Simon Marcson told him, "The only reason I would consider moving out [of research] would be if I felt that the new crop of people were more adequate than I am. I don't want to live a life of quiet desperation. . . ."[19] But a man who waits

until he is in his late thirties or early forties before deciding that he wants to move into administration is likely to
be told that he has waited too long. There are exceptions,
of course. But a man who has spent fifteen years as a problem solver, competently handling whatever came his way
but never initiating new lines of research, is not ordinarily
thought of as a good candidate for a job as a manager of
research, or of anything else.

A scientist who finds himself in this situation does not
usually have to worry about money. Few companies are so
hardhearted as to fire a man who has, so to speak, given his
employers the best years of his life. He may be offered a
liaison job, in which he will be expected to keep the company's central research organization posted on what the
operating divisions need and want, and to keep the divisions posted on what is going on in central research. Or he
may be set to work sifting through scientific and technological literature and reports for useful ideas. Usually he
just keeps on doing research. But the problems he is given
tend more and more to be routine, and as time goes on he
puts less and less effort into solving them. Although he
shows up for work every day, he tends to be more concerned with outside activities than with the laboratory. He
is likely to serve on his local school board, and to help run
community fund drives. In effect, after fifteen or twenty
years of professional life he goes into semiretirement.*

---

* Given the shortage of good science teachers, this is a deplorable
waste of talent. Big corporations, which in many cases give money regularly to colleges, might well encourage scientists in their employ to do a
certain amount of college teaching—not as moonlighters, but on company
time—with the understanding that after, say, fifteen years a man could
if he wished give as much as half or even two-thirds of his time to teaching, without having to take a cut in salary. This would be good not only
for the colleges, but for the researcher who finds himself superannuated
at forty.

Industrial research managers often complain about how seldom the scientists who work for them come up with bright and original ideas. This is only partly accounted for by the fact that very bright and original young scientists usually do not take jobs in industry. It is also clear that in most industrial research organizations the climate is unfavorable to ideas that are daring or radical.

Change upsets business organizations, and is bound to be strenuously resisted. "The greatest durability contest in the world is getting a new idea into any factory," a former head of research at General Motors once observed. "It is well if the management understands this and will constitute itself the sales department for the research organization. Otherwise, the hard-boiled men in the factory will put the research men out of business in a fortnight." He added, "The most pitiable thing in the world is a man who does not know how terrible factory organizations are. Putting a research man up against it is like throwing Daniel to the lions when they are all hungry."[20] These remarks were made more than twenty-five years ago, and factory organizations, at least in industries in which rapid technological change is taken for granted, no longer manhandle researchers as they once did. But men in charge of manufacturing and sales typically feel that the scientist's main job is not to think up ideas for new products and processes, which are as likely as not to be impractical, but rather to help the manufacturing and sales departments solve the immediate problems that confront them. In a company where the top management shares this attitude, a scientist may conclude that being creative, except as a troubleshooter, doesn't pay off.

Indeed, a scientist who has a good (but radical) idea may have to choose between forgetting about it and risking his job in order to prove its feasibility. An instance of this situation was described not long ago by Arthur K. Watson, President of the IBM World Trade Corporation. "The disk memory unit, the heart of today's random access computer, is not the logical outcome of a decision made by IBM management," he told an audience of accountants. "It was developed in one of our laboratories as a bootleg project—over the stern warning from management that the project had to be dropped because of budget difficulties. A handful of men ignored the warning. They broke the rules. They risked their jobs to work on a project they believed in."[21]

One could argue that if a scientist chooses to disregard the judgment of his superiors in the corporate hierarchy and to carry on with a project that they see no point in, he should be willing to stake his job on the outcome. Some companies, however, think this is too much to ask. They believe there are times when a researcher should be given the time, money, and assistance he feels he needs in order to prove—by building a prototype of a new device, for example—the validity of an idea that the company's manufacturing and development people have said they do not consider worth pursuing. James B. Fisk, president of the Bell Telephone Laboratories, has argued that if research is to flourish in an industrial setting, it is not enough that the researcher be sheltered from the importunities of harried plant managers. He must also have "the freedom occasionally to carry ideas experimentally into the application stage to a point where merit can be demonstrated, when the researcher considers that his merit has not been recognized or has been overshadowed by development schedule pressure."[22] One result of denying scientists a chance to do this has been described in an article in the *Harvard Business Review*. The authors cite the case of a large company that does a lot of research, but whose budget makes

no provision for the exploratory development of new processes and devices. "Operating groups thus accept almost
no new research technology," they write. "Researchers
have become so frustrated at not seeing their results used
that many have left the company. The home town of the
large company is now ringed with small businesses started
by these researchers."[23]

Originality and imagination in industrial research are
also discouraged by the fact that the way a scientist in
industry thinks is less important, by and large, than how he
behaves. There are scientists who do manage to get ahead
purely by exercising their intellectual prowess. But money,
freedom and power are more commonly won by exercising
nonintellectual skills of the kind that are rewarded in other
walks of corporate life.

To begin with, salesmanship counts heavily. When a scientist in industry suggests a particular line of investigation,
or a particular attack on a problem, acceptance of his
proposal may depend less on its intrinsic merit than on
his ability to convince other people, who are not scientists,
of its commercial or technological relevance. This skill is
perhaps most highly valued in laboratories that do a great
deal of research under government contract. Senior staff
people at such laboratories spend a lot of time writing up
proposals for new projects and trying to persuade prospective clients to support them. "We put a lot of emphasis on
communication, both oral and written," I was told by the
personnel manager of a laboratory that works mainly for
the National Aeronautics and Space Administration. "I
wouldn't care if you could guarantee me a man is a genius,
I wouldn't hire him if he's not articulate." Chris Argyris, a
professor of industrial administration at Yale, reported
after studying a number of industrial research organizations that in every one "the majority of the members reported that in addition to technical competence, 'selling,'

'being articulate,' 'knowing the right people,' 'being on a project that paid off,' were very important qualities for success."[24]

A researcher who is very persuasive in arguing that a particular line of investigation that he wants to follow is likely to yield big practical returns may, of course, be a first-rate scientist. But it does not follow that a persuasive scientist is necessarily good, or that a scientist who is awkward and tongue-tied is bad. One of the main jobs of an administrator of an industrial laboratory should be to sell the company's management on the ideas of scientists in his department or division who don't know how to sell, and to shoot down the proposals of researchers who are better salesmen than they are scientists.

Unfortunately, laboratory administrators themselves are probably more often picked for persuasiveness than for brains, and may have a lot of difficulty themselves in telling good ideas from bad.* Also, scientists who cross the line into administration tend rather quickly to lose touch with scientists who still do research. As a leader of a small, informal working group, a man may continue to think like a scientist, and he may act less like a boss than like someone who has been elected by the members of the group to represent them in negotiations with management. But if he accepts a full-time job as a research manager, he must learn to think, at least in part, like management, and at this stage many men stop thinking at all like researchers. Often, Lowell Steele points out, they are impelled to do so by guilt. A scientist who becomes an administrator may be haunted by a feeling that he has sold out. One way of dealing with this anxiety is to suppress it by cutting oneself

---

* The 3,500 scientists and engineers covered by the survey cited earlier in this chapter were asked, "Do present selection procedures provide the best supervisors?" Two-thirds answered No. The same answer was given by half of the supervisors to whom the question was put.

off from his former colleagues and going over permanently to the enemy camp. In every industrial laboratory one meets administrators who spend their lunch hours talking about golf and the stock market, and who justify their decision to become managers by adopting the view that scientists on the whole are an irresponsible and self-indulgent lot who think the world owes them a living. Even managers who feel no need to erect defenses of this kind tend to lose touch with the people they once worked with. Steele quotes a young mathematician who told him, "Research management carries within itself the seeds of its own destruction. If a man stays in management, sooner or later he will reach a point where he no longer understands research or the people who do it. It is inevitable. It would happen to me, too."[25]

Salesmanship is not the only nonintellectual talent that pays off in industrial research. Young scientists are also given high marks for tact, dependability, and the ability to work smoothly with other people. Some of the biggest (and best) laboratories do tolerate a certain number of oddballs who like to work at night, or who are incapable of meeting deadlines, or who refuse to tell their supervisors what they are up to. Often, however, their position is like that of a pet Jew; they are valued by the laboratory's management mainly because their presence proves that what the laboratory really cares about is not sterile conformity, but creativity. But many laboratories take great pains to screen out scientists with the wrong kind of personalities. In *Scientists and Industry: Conflict and Accommodation*, William Kornhauser of the University of California reports that at one company he studied, where roughly 10 percent of the central research staff was recruited each year for jobs in the company's operating divisions or in corporate management, the research director made it clear that he didn't want "scientist's scientists," but, rather, men with "leadership qualities." He explained, "Those not aggressive enough to hold their own may be left after the company takes the best people. We have to protect ourselves not to be overwhelmed by people who can't become leaders." The director added that what he looked for in prospects was "ease of interviewing, not too quiet, handles himself well with other people, ready to be part of the team, can share problems and not try to run with the ball or be a shining light, communicates well, has broad interests. . . ."[26]

An aptitude for organizational politics is also a valuable asset in industrial research. A scientist who wants to be able to carry out his ideas, or simply to get ahead in the organization, stands a much better chance if he knows how to bide his time, how to line up powerful allies, and how to avoid the traps that enemies may lay for him. In the words of Morris Stein, a psychologist who has examined the criteria by which chemists are judged in industrial research, "In all relationships [the researcher] is expected to be sincere, honest, purposeful, and diplomatic, but not unwilling to accept 'shortcuts,' be flexible, and Machiavellian."[27] In particular, the neophyte must take care not to seem brash or overeager. This is one of the principal messages of an article called "Introduction of the Newly Graduated Scientist to Industrial Research," published in 1960 by the magazine *Research Management*. The author, a staff specialist employed by the Sun Oil Company, emphasizes how important it is for a new recruit to be modest, and adds, "Still another problem is that of the impact of corporate policies, ways of doing things, communication channels, etc. upon the neophyte scientist who is at the stage of his life where he is properly most eager to accomplish great things. He may soon discover that his earnest and well-intentioned efforts may have earned him the unofficial yet damning title of 'boat rocker.'" The author goes on to recall the words of a chemistry professor who always warned his graduate students that they should not try to change company or laboratory policies until they had become part of the group charged with making and carrying out such policies. "This is good, conservative advice," he writes, "unless one likes to live dangerously and has other dependable sources of income."[28]

A laboratory in which young scientists are evaluated by the same standards as junior executives is unlikely to produce many daring or brilliant ideas. In a situation where salary and title are regarded as the only true measure of a man's worth, and where these have little to do with the quality of his purely scientific or technical achievements, getting ahead in the organization can easily become an end in itself. A scientist may decide with reason that the best way to attain this end is to put his efforts into organizational politics instead of science. As Herbert Shepard has written, "There is a good deal of evidence that a scientist does his best work when he becomes almost totally preoccupied with a scientific puzzle of his own choice. Instead, we find many scientists who are preoccupied with puzzles stemming from the status and salary system. Some have either lost or never developed the capacity for choosing their own puzzles, let alone becoming preoccupied with them. But the status and salary systems do not necessarily help such scientists to develop this capacity. They are more likely to motivate the scientists to find out what puzzles they are supposed to pretend to be preoccupied with in order to get higher status and pay, or more generally to find a way of beating the system."[29]

There are first-rate scientists who are also first-rate politicians, and who use their political skill to secure the privilege of doing what they want to do as researchers. But politics and truth are in a sense incompatible, and a scientist who sets out to use politics to advance a scientific career may be taking the first step toward abandoning it.

He may become so political in his thinking and his habits that he can no longer submit himself to the quite different discipline of scientific thought, which has no use for consensus or compromise, or for the deceptions that are indispensable in politics.

In 1959, the Opinion Research Corporation of Princeton, New Jersey, acting on behalf of the clients of its Public Opinion Index for Industry, questioned some six hundred scientists and engineers employed by six large companies. It asked them, among other things, how they liked their jobs. Only 34 percent said they were "very well satisfied," and this group included only 42 percent of those whom the management of their companies rated as "most valuable." Noting that similar surveys of foremen, office supervisors, and other white collar workers in industry had produced quite different results, Opinion Research concluded, "Despite considerable attention from management, scientists and engineers remain one of the most disgruntled groups on industry's payroll."[30]

The pervading discontent to which these figures point can be fully accounted for only by considering the situation of the scientific workers in industry who do not have doctorates, a group that outnumbers those with Ph.D.'s by perhaps five to one. Some of these scientists and engineers take industrial jobs mainly to earn money so that they can go back to school and get their Ph.D.'s later, or to support themselves and their families while they finish their graduate work on a part-time basis. Many men who do this leave industry as soon as they have their doctorates, and get teaching jobs at colleges or universities. There are also people in industry who have won the privilege of working on their own, and who do first-rate work, even though they have no Ph.D.'s and therefore occupy a somewhat ambiguous social position, like a naval officer who has been promoted from the ranks. A larger number abandon research to become salesmen, production supervisors, plant managers, or leaders of groups engaged in systems engineering or in developing new products.

But most of the tens of thousands of young college graduates with bachelor's or master's degrees in science or engineering who go to work in industrial laboratories each year become part of an intellectual proletariat. This is not to say that they all end up as laboratory technicians. Some do, but many more spend at least part of their time on tasks that call for judgment, ingenuity, and a great deal of professional skill. The terms on which this work has to be done, however, are often such as to cause great bitterness and frustration. While the laboratory's star scientists are off reading papers at international meetings in Rome or Tokyo, and while the company's research managers are buying power cruisers and building new houses, the average scientist or engineer in industry works in anonymity and for relatively little money. In 1964, for example, physicists without advanced degrees who were working in industrial research and development earned an average of $10,000 a year, while physicists with Ph.D.'s were averaging $15,000 as researchers, and $21,000 if they were in administration.[31] Another source of frustration is the fact that the average industrial researcher has little more choice about what he does to earn his living than a worker on an assembly line. Laboratory policy may specify that he may spend 10 or even 20 percent of his time working on projects of his own. But he is likely to conclude—usually rightly—that he will get ahead faster if he uses the time to carry on with his assigned work. Moreover, he cannot turn down an assignment because he thinks it is pointless. And he cannot turn it down because its purpose is, for example, to develop a new shampoo that is no better than its competitors, but that is just different enough so that the copywriters will have a new miracle ingredient to write about. He can, of course, quit his job. But unlike the scientist with a Ph.D., he has little choice except to look for another job in industry, in which he may be no better off than he was before.

In these circumstances, it would not be surprising if most researchers in industry would like nothing better than to stop doing research. This would seem, in fact, to be the case. Morris Stein asked a group of industrial chemists what they would like their companies to do for them if they should succeed in developing a major new product. Of the twelve possible rewards on a list prepared by Stein, the most popular choice was "Make you assistant to the research director," and the next most popular was "Send you to an executive training program." "Permit you to choose your own problems" and "Give you more people to carry out your ideas" were in sixth and seventh place, just after "Give you administrative experience in other divisions within the company."[32] The attitudes revealed by Stein's question go a long way toward explaining why industrial research is inefficient. There are not nearly enough management jobs for everybody, and the engineer or scientist who realizes he is probably never going to get one, and is therefore condemned to labor at tasks that will frequently be tedious, or foolish, or both, obviously has no particular reason to throw himself into his work with the enthusiasm that his superiors would like to see. Instead, he is likely to fall into an attitude of cynicism and resignation, in which he derives less satisfaction from his work than from the ingenuity with which he contrives to avoid doing it.

IX

Movers and Shakers

Robert c. wood, an M.I.T. professor who has taken an interest in the political attitudes and roles of American scientists, points out that scientists very often see themselves as "specially endowed to bring order and sense to the political process." Wood has described in detail what scientists conceive this endowment to be. "Not responsible for past errors in public policy," he writes, "carrying the keys which will unlock the doors to a better way of life for all, and capable of bringing order out of political chaos, the scientists can enter the decision making process secure in the knowledge that their activities are not impelled by personal ambition and the thirst for power." Wood adds, "Reluctantly, they emerge from the laboratory at the time of a great emergency to save the nation or the world. . . . They sacrifice professional careers in the interests of an informed debate on great public issues. Their function in the controversies over space, missile systems, or education is not to find new glory or power for their power group, to promote new funds for a pet project, or to protect a vested interest. Rather their mission is to assure that the wellsprings of creative achievement continue to flow, and that the same characteristics of reason, logic, respect for individualism, and objectivity are brought to bear on problems of human relations. Compared to the self-seeking, the parochialism, and the limited knowledge of other participants, the scientists offer the welcome contrast of prescient men concerned only with explaining and using the powers of nature. . . ."[1]

Wood is not claiming that scientists really are this way. But the fact that many scientists would consider what he has written to be a fair, if somewhat idealized, likeness marks a striking change in the relationship between scientists and politicians. Before World War Two, American scientists would have rejected as absurd the idea that they might have anything to contribute to the process of government other than advice on narrowly defined technical questions. But in the glow of Hiroshima and Nagasaki, scientists, and especially physicists, appeared in a new light. S. K. Allison, a scientist who worked on the atom bomb, has written, "Suddenly physicists were exhibited as lions at Washington tea parties, were invited to conventions of social scientists, where their opinions on society were respectfully listened to by life-long experts in the field, attended conventions of religious orders and discoursed on theology, were asked to endorse plans for world government, and to give simplified lectures on the nucleus to Congressional committees."[2] Scientists, for their part, were for the first time trying to make their voices heard in politics. They were driven to do this by a conviction that they knew better than other men the nature of the genie they had let out of the bottle, and that it was their duty to see to it that the genie was brought under proper control. There was even a hope that the bomb might shock mankind out of its complacency, and usher in an era in which politicians and diplomats, acting under the tutelage of scientists, would take radical and sweeping measures to make war impossible.

The hope, of course, faded. But scientists and government officials kept up the sort of collaboration, aimed

mainly at finding solutions to problems of military strategy
and technology, that had been so successful during the
war. Then in 1957 the Russians launched the first artificial
satellite, and American scientists were cast as saviors who
alone could rescue the nation from the dire consequences
of its technological shortcomings. Politicians began to ask
their advice on a wide variety of matters with much the
same uncritical enthusiasm as Franklin D. Roosevelt dis-
played toward economists in the early years of the New
Deal.

As an Ohio congressman, Charles Mosher, has pointed
out, politicians have outgrown the "gee-whiz" stage in
their dealing with scientists. Speaking of the House Committee on Science and Astronautics, of which he is a member, Mosher has observed, "It no longer seems overwhelmed by the magnitude and complexity of the new
environment in which it is expected to operate. The . . .
members are no longer overawed in the presence of the
famous scientists who have come before it as witnesses and
advisors."[3]

But the scientists who were urgently summoned to
Washington in the late 1950's are still there, or have been
succeeded by other scientists, and American scientists
probably have more to say about the way their government is run than do the scientists of any other major country. They not only operate the machinery by which the
government distributes patronage to researchers, but they
have succeeded, by and large, in seeing to it that this patronage is available in generous amounts and on generous
terms. Leading scientists, both in and out of government,
are regularly consulted, and very often listened to, when
important technological decisions have to be made. Scientists are also asked for advice (though their advice is not
so often followed) on questions that are only in part sci-

entific or technological—questions such as whether to build an antiballistic missile defense system, or where the main emphasis should be placed in the space program after a man has been landed on the moon. Many government agencies have full-time scientific advisers, and part-time advisory councils, and since 1957 the President has had a full-time Special Assistant for Science and Technology. The Assistant is assisted by an eighteen-man group, the President's Science Advisory Committee, or P-SAC, which in turn is assisted by dozens of scientific advisory panels brought together to study specific questions. So many scientists now spend so much time in Washington that the term "political scientist" has come to have a double meaning.

Washington scientists may be divided into two groups: those who administer and those who advise. (Some, of course, do both.) A few of the administrators have risen to levels of government where they manage other things besides research and development. This small group includes, to name one of its most conspicuous members, Harold Brown, Secretary of the Air Force, who has a Ph.D. in physics from Columbia. But the great majority are research administrators, whose job is to make sure that the government gets good value for the large sums of money it invests in research and development. Some of these administrators are men who have made their mark as researchers and then, in middle age, have moved into high-level jobs in government, in much the same way as other scientists become deans and presidents of universities. Glenn Seaborg, a Nobel laureate in chemistry, was actually chancellor of the University of California at Berkeley before he went to Washington in 1961 as chairman of the Atomic Energy Commission. More commonly, however, government research administrators are men who gave up research in their twenties or very early thirties to become career civil servants.

Men make this change for many different reasons. Lewis C. Mainzer, a political scientist in the old-fashioned meaning of the term, reported after interviewing seventy-five administrators of federal research programs that "administrative power is for some a quiet haven and merely a job, for some an end in itself and a joy, for some a means to the top, and for some a sober duty—a self-sacrifice—to science, to colleagues, to noble purpose."[4]

As one high-ranking administrator with whom I spoke pointed out, an administrative job in Washington can also give a scientist the invigorating sense of helping to shape the course of history. This official, a cultivated and articulate man in his early fifties, began his administrative career in World War Two, just three years after he had gotten a Ph.D. in mathematics at Harvard, when the Army put him in charge of a small applied-research project. He has been an administrator ever since, and at the time I talked with him he was deputy chief of research of an agency that had been one of the first in Washington to give generous support to university scientists. "At the beginning, although I was an administrator, I was personally involved in science," he said. "I suppose I was theoretically capable of writing perhaps half of the papers that were written by the people whose research I was supporting. But as one proceeds in administration, one loses first the patience for research, and finally even the eye for detail. I didn't mind, though. In those years, in the late nineteen-forties and early nineteen-fifties, I was riding an irresistible wave—the mathematicization, you might say, of military technology and operations. We were learning to use mathematics to optimize the use of machines and people. Many of the research programs we were putting into effect had existed for years in my mind, and I was able to move with considerable assurance, crystallizing the paths along which major efforts should be launched. Soon the work was on such a scale that I could no longer read all the papers that I was 'producing,' as it were. In time, as my responsibilities broadened, I became less concerned with mathematics as such. I became fascinated with such questions as how relevant technology can be made to emerge from the stuff of scientific knowledge and insight, and what part the research administrator could play in the process. We tried many experiments. I think I was one of the first people to bring behavioral and social scientists—even historians—into the mix."

He smiled, and went on to say, "You know, sometimes in the early days I would ask myself why I was doing this, instead of putting my six feet of immortal works on the bookshelves of history—which I was brought up from the cradle to think was the only right thing for a scientist to do. If you write important papers, and publish important books, your name will be there for all the world to see. But the reason I look back with satisfaction on these years is that I am aware of what the alternative course of history might have been in certain instances. This does not have quite the same material existence as papers and books. But in a history-rich era such as ours, many roads meet in the wood, and to have been instrumental in helping to choose the right road—that is rather important."

Men like this scientist have had a great deal of influence on the evolution of military and space technology, and on the quality of scientific research in certain fields. But by and large, men who manage government research programs have had less to do with shaping government policies than scientists whose job is to advise. Some advisers are, like administrators, full-time government employees, who have no ties to universities or other nongovernmental institutions. In general, however, the most influential scientists in Washington are those whose base of operations is elsewhere—in Cambridge, say, or Berkeley, or Pasadena. Often these are men who spend two or three days a month in Washington attending meetings of advisory panels, conferring with generals and heads of agencies, and lunching at the Cosmos Club, an elegant Renaissance mansion on Massachusetts Avenue frequented by movers and shakers in scientific affairs. Other advisors are scientists-in-residence, but only for a time; it is understood that after two or three years at the most they will be returning to Cal Tech or I.B.M. or Columbia.

The extent to which scientists are in demand as part-time advisers, and the variety of matters on which their advice is sought, are pointed up in an article by Bernice Eiduson.[5] In 1964, Dr. Eiduson reinterviewed the subjects of her book, *Scientists: Their Psychological World*, and found that eighteen of the thirty-nine surviving members of the group were consultants to government agencies. Among the things they had been consulted about, she reported, were the control of narcotics, technical aspects of foreign aid, the Geneva test-ban agreement, ways to bring about exchanges of scientists with countries in the Soviet bloc, the deployment of manpower in the United States, the probable future demand for Ph.D.'s, educational and scientific aid to underdeveloped countries, the evaluation of drugs such as thalidomide, and the school dropout problem.

Scientists who go to Washington as consultants fall into three categories. The majority go as members of review panels whose only job is to study research proposals and evaluate their scientific merits. A smaller number go as members of committees or study groups whose job is to give specialized technical advice—for example, to advise the Navy on "long-range scientific and technical problems related to defensive and offensive mine warfare," or to advise the AEC on geologic aspects of its program for disposing of radioactive wastes. Finally there are the scientists, numbering perhaps two hundred and fifty in all, whom James R. Killian, Jr., the first man to hold the job of Presidential Assistant for Science and Technology, has characterized as "consistently influential" in government affairs.

These are the scientists who have easy access to the heads of agencies, or to their principal deputies, and whose advice is solicited in important matters that are as much social and political as they are scientific and technological. Their opinions may be asked, for example, on how to translate new biological knowledge more quickly into better medical care, or on the soundness of a proposed bill for controlling air pollution. Scientists who are called on for this sort of advice are, in many cases, the same men who represent the scientific community, or subcommunities, in the bargaining that determines how much money the government spends for research and what the money is spent for. Thus Frederick Seitz, a former professor of physics at the University of Illinois, is not only a member of P-SAC and chairman of the Defense Science Board, which is the Defense Department's principal scientific advisory body, he is also president of the National Academy of Sciences, a semipublic institution which is both an honorary society and the House of Bishops of American science. This double role is also played, to give one more example, by Harvey Brooks, Dean of Engineering and Applied Physics at Harvard, who has been one of the most consulted of the Washington consultants in recent years. Brooks is one of several "consultants at large" to P-SAC (of which he is a former member), and at the same time is chairman of the National Academy's Committee on Science and Public Policy, known acronymically as COSPUP, which acts as a sort of executive committee of the scientific establishment. He has also been a spokesman for his own particular segment of the scientific community, serving as a member of the Academy's Physics Survey Committee, which not long ago recommended, among other things, a 150 percent increase, over a six-year period, in federal outlays for the support of physical research.

Who are the scientists who become "consistently influential" as advisers and in the management of scientific affairs? A few are employed in industry—in several cases by the Bell Telephone Laboratories. A few, like Alvin Weinberg of Oak Ridge, are or have been administrators of research programs at national laboratories. But more often than not, scientists who carry weight in Washington have spent most or all of their professional lives at universities—typically at one of the leading universities. At one time, for instance, six of the eighteen members of P-SAC were based at either Harvard or M.I.T., and the current membership of COSPUP, which has fifteen members, includes three scientists from the University of California, two from Chicago, and one each from Harvard, Yale, Johns Hopkins, Wisconsin, Michigan, and M.I.T.*

Scientists picked for high-level advisory panels and committees are recruited by other scientists who hold advisory jobs. Since it is impossible to tell from a man's scientific papers whether he will be any good as a committeeman, the leaders of the Washington establishment have tended to pick men they know and have worked with. Almost all the scientists called to Washington in the 1940's were men who had worked on one of the big wartime projects, and they were inclined to choose as their

* This does not sit too well with other institutions. University X, which would like the government to locate a big new radio telescope at a site easily accessible to members of X's astronomy department, is obviously more likely to get its way if the department chairman is commuting to Washington as a consultant, and knows his way around there.

lieutenants and eventual successors men of similar experience. Jerome Wiesner, who was President Kennedy's Special Assistant for Science and Technology, worked on radar
at M.I.T. during the war; his predecessor, George Kistiakowsky, a Harvard professor, and his successor, Donald
Hornig, a Princeton professor, both worked on the bomb at
Los Alamos. Of the younger men who have been taken into
the club, several, including Harold Brown, were research
administrators at the AEC's weapons laboratory in Livermore, California. A number of others are, or have been,
members of Jason, a group of scientists (mostly from universities and mostly physicists) who meet for six weeks
each summer to study problems of concern to the Department of Defense. Many of these problems are strictly scientific or technological, but from time to time Jason members are also given a crack at questions of a "softer" variety
—that is, requiring political or psychological or economic
as well as scientific judgments.

Scientists who become influential in Washington usually
are, or have been at one time, quite successful as researchers; if a man has never done anything but mediocre scientific work, his political and organizing talents, however
dazzling, are likely to be discounted by the scientific community. They also tend to have, or to develop, certain
other aptitudes and traits that set them apart from the general run of scientists. In the opinion of the scientists whom
Dr. Eiduson questioned, it is important for a consultant to
be sensitive to other people's ideas; to be forceful—"If
you're not forceful, you won't be listened to, because there
are a lot of people in Washington trying to get their ideas
across"; to be able to make decisions without worrying too
much about details; and to be able to "live with the consequences of decisions without becoming too obsessive and
constantly debating with yourself whether you have made
the right decision. . . ."[6] It is also useful to have a lot of

staying power. An astronomer who spends a good deal of time in Washington told me, "There is some kind of stamina—brain stamina—that is necessary. When I was young, I didn't realize I had it. But I have found that at committee meetings I can outstay other people in paying full attention to the matter in hand. There have been times when I have exploited this talent shamelessly." This scientist went on to touch on two other points often made by old Washington hands. "When one gets involved in government advising, one finds oneself very ineffective if one tries to influence things for one or two years ahead," he said. "Everybody's already made up his mind about what's to be done in that period. You have to think in a much longer time span to have a chance to influence what really happens. This is very hard for a scientist to learn and accept. Also, you have to make up your mind on what a scientist would consider very unsafe grounds. But if you abdicate your responsibility, decisions will be made by people who are maybe even less qualified than you are."

Finally, scientists who do well in Washington tend to have a large tolerance for personal conflict and political maneuvering. "You're always dealing with people," a former university professor and dean, now a full-time adviser and panel organizer, points out. "If you are going to make a career out of these advisory activities, you have to be the kind of person who gets enjoyment out of other people's idiosyncrasies. Success—getting your point of view across—isn't enough to keep you going. Even when things go badly, I find it amusing just to be part of the show."

One of the main troubles that scientists have in dealing with politicians is that in general they shrink from the clash of wills, ambitions, and personalities that politicians take in their stride. Summarizing a number of studies of the personalities of productive scientists, Anne Roe writes,

"Their interpersonal relations are generally of low intensity. They are reported to be ungregarious, not talkative (this does not apply to social scientists) and rather asocial. . . . They dislike interpersonal controversy in any form and are especially sensitive to interpersonal aggression. . . . They show much stronger preoccupation with things and ideas than with people. . . ."[7] One can predict with confidence that a scientist who fits this description will be both miserable and ineffective in Washington.

Not all scientists are as misanthropic and gun-shy as Dr. Roe's psychological sketch suggests. Some find consulting agreeable and exciting. Scientists are probably no more immune than anyone else to the heady feeling that comes with being at, or near, the center of political power, and of having a hand in affairs of great moment—though scientists may be more reluctant to admit their susceptibility. "Everybody loves to be needed, and to have an influence," one scientist told Dr. Eiduson. "For me it flatters my ego. There is nothing altruistic about it. It's pleasant to hobnob with generals and Cabinet officers. I'm not doing this work out of duty but out of snobbery—out of a competition for prestige—a peculiar kind of prestige that's not scientific or public. It's stupid, perhaps, but it flatters my ego. It's like newspaper write-ups or appearing in *Life* magazine. It gives you a special kind of excitement."

Other scientists, while not denying that it is fun to hobnob with Cabinet officers, say they find other satisfactions in work they do for the government. They say it is refreshing to address themselves to questions quite different from those they deal with in their laboratories, and that it gives them a gratifying sense of power to be doing something that may have an enormous impact on the nonscientific world. This is perhaps most often true of scientists who, like a distinguished physicist named *David Windham,* mainly give advice of a technical and scientific kind. During World War Two, Windham, who is now in his middle fifties, worked on radar at M.I.T. In 1946 he went back to the university where he had been an instructor before the war, but over the next ten years he put in a good deal of time as a member of various summer study groups. These consisted of scientists and engineers brought together by the government in the hope they might find answers to questions such as how best to deal with enemy submarines in a future war, or whether the Defense Department should put a lot of money and effort into developing intercontinental ballistic missiles.

"These study groups were a continuation of a wartime relationship between scientists and people in the government that had proved quite fruitful," Windham told me. "There were very thorny problems. The submarine threat was a very difficult one to cope with. What we had to offer was a fresh, nontraditional approach. The government would get us in and just let us hack around. In the anti-submarine study, we were able to work outside Navy doctrine. One of our proposals, for example, was for the United States to build faster merchant ships. It was often interesting to get that much of an inside view of a problem. On the whole I think people enjoyed doing this work. The people who didn't enjoy it didn't do it."

In 1957, Windham became a member of P-SAC, and began spending two or three days a month in Washington. Many of the problems he dealt with were purely technological—for instance, whether the development of clustered-rocket engines was the best way of catching up with the Russians in rocket propulsion. But President Eisenhower also called frequently on committee members for advice in matters that were political as well as technical. There was, for example, the question of whether the United States should try for a treaty banning nuclear weapons tests, an issue on which American scientists sharply disagreed. Like most other members of P-SAC, Windham was in favor of the treaty, and he was drawn into a certain amount of political skirmishing with the antitreaty forces; these were led by Edward Teller, the director of the nuclear weapons laboratory at Livermore. "We had to shoot down missiles from Livermore that were intended to torpedo the test ban," Windham said. "But except on this issue, I felt just as free from any sort of political pressure as you can imagine."

In recent years, Windham's work in Washington has been almost entirely on technical problems. "For many of us who got started on this sort of thing during the war, working on these problems has become as much a part of our profession as the work we do in our own fields," he said. "The work I do for the government still takes up as much time as any single other piece of my life. I'm not a terribly well-organized individual, and so this work has been more of a distraction for me than it would be for someone who schedules his effort better. But I really haven't the slightest feeling that I have made fewer contributions of a strictly scientific kind because I have helped the government. As a matter of fact, the work I did after the war was a direct outgrowth of the work I had done at the Radiation Laboratory at M.I.T., and of the associations I made there. Of course, most of the problem solving I do for the government is quite remote from my own scientific interests. But in many ways I'm an engineer by taste and training, and I've enjoyed this kind of all-purpose activity. It's an amusing way to use what I know."

Much the same point was made by another physicist, who is a member of the Jason group. "The work is completely separate from what I do here at Chicago," he said. "I welcome it for that reason. I find it very pleasant to flex my muscles on practical things." He added that the pleas-

ure is enhanced by the fact that the group does its summer muscle-flexing at such agreeable locations as Woods
Hole, Santa Barbara, and La Jolla.

Often, however, scientists who are recruited for Washington duty are depressed and frustrated by what they find
there. This was true of most of the men studied by Dr.
Eiduson. "Uniformly," she writes, "they noted that there
was very little awareness of the scientist, and very little
indication that he was making any impact." One man told
her, "Now we are blasé and we do not regret what we've
done; but we were certainly naïve to think we could contribute anywhere near what we thought we could, and
naïve to think that our services would be demanded by the
total government." Five of the scientists in the group said
they had been misused, typically by politicians who tried
to play them off against other scientists. But "the greatest
single source of frustration for the entire group lay in their
being asked for advice, but seldom listened to."[8]
All of the scientists interviewed by Dr. Eiduson agreed
that to do a good job as an adviser, and to have the best
chance of getting one's advice accepted, it is almost essential to spend all one's time in Washington. But they also
said that to become a full-time adviser is in a way self-
defeating. "A full-time Washingtonian loses touch with his
university and with research, and once this happens, he
can no longer be considered a first-rate scientist," Dr.
Eiduson writes. "This weakens his effectiveness, and even
his worth to Washington. . . . While effectiveness goes
hand in hand with a strong scientific reputation, scientists
also appreciate that the longer they stay in Washington,
the more they lose their identity as scientists. To others, as
well as to themselves, they become merged with lawyers
and politicians, and all the 'advice-givers' who have pre-
ceded them."

With one exception, Dr. Eiduson's scientists said they had decided to spend less time in Washington, and had freed themselves from many or most of their commitments. Some said they felt they could not go on indefinitely asking other faculty members to cover for them while they were away. Some had grown worried because they weren't getting any research done. Some said they were cutting down on their work in Washington because they had come to hate it. "I was becoming a government committee figure," one man said. "It was really big business. I found myself doing unpleasant things with people I despised and even before I knew it, I was finding myself trying to rival them. Then I realized that I was really selling out my soul to them. . . . Now I see other kids doing what I was doing and I know very well that they are not doing it too well because they're too young—and I say, 'Look at those sons-of-guns wasting their time the way I did in Washington.' I ought to tell them not to do it—but I won't because somebody's got to do it, and this way it doesn't have to be me. It's an emotionally revolting and emotionally draining experience."

Scientists who go to Washington as advisers often have good reason to be angry. A politician may have no intention of following the advice he has asked for unless it turns out to agree with his own ideas of what should, or can, be done. Frequently he contrives to eat his cake and have it too: if he likes the recommendations he gets, he uses them as a weapon against his political opponents; if he doesn't like them, he buries them and arranges for the appointment of another panel. This practice has been criticized by, among others, Philip H. Abelson, director of the Geophysical Laboratory of the Carnegie Institution of Washington, and editor of *Science*. Referring to the advisory panels to which problems are farmed out by the President's Special Assist-

ant for Science and Technology and by P-SAC, Abelson
has written, "Actually the panel system has serious potential weaknesses. Brilliant men come to Washington for a
few days, are given detailed briefings, and then, with a
limited amount of time for consideration, form opinions on
matters that may involve tremendous sums of money and
even the security of the nation." He adds, "Their eventual
recommendations can be manipulated by controlling the
nature of the briefings. Their report, when issued, is in
general not a public document. Thus, if it is not convenient
to implement the conclusions, the report can be pigeon-
holed."[9]

But the frustration and disgust felt by many scientists
who go to Washington can not be blamed entirely on the
deceitfulness of politicians. Their difficulties sometimes
arise from naïve assumptions, summarized by Robert
Wood in the passage quoted at the beginning of this chapter, about the part scientists are fitted to play in government and politics. Among these assumptions is the belief
that scientists are more prescient than other men. In the
words of C. P. Snow, scientists have "the future in their
bones."[10] Therefore, Snow argues, they have "something
to give which our kind of existential society is desperately
short of: so short of, that it fails to recognize of what it is
starved. That is foresight." Foresight, Snow adds, is "not
quite knowledge," but "much more an expectation of
knowledge to come . . . something that a scientist, if he has
this kind of sensitivity latent in him, picks up during his
scientific experience."[11]

This claim has been critically examined by Albert Wohlstetter, a leading practitioner of the new art, or science, of
strategic analysis. In an essay called "Strategy and the Natural Scientists," Wohlstetter concedes that "many scientists have had extremely penetrating and useful percep-
tions from time to time on the major problems that beset

us." But, he adds, "the belief that they have been right and ordinary humans wrong will hardly sustain a look at the record of policies on cardinal choices recommended by physical scientists and engineers since the last war." Wohlstetter then turns to what "is perhaps the most frequently cited example of superior scientific prescience"—that is, the accuracy with which American scientists were able to predict how long it would take the Soviet Union to develop an atomic bomb.[12]

Some scientists, he writes, were good prophets. But some were bad, and in some cases the same scientist made both good and bad prophecies. Eugene Rabinowitch, the editor of *Bulletin of the Atomic Scientists*, was among the signers, in 1945, of the so-called Franck Report, which accurately predicted that the Russians would have the bomb within five years or so. In 1948, however, only a little more than a year before the Russians exploded their first nuclear device, Rabinowitch changed his forecast and surmised that Russia "probably expects to acquire [atomic bombs] in five or ten years." The distinguished American physicist, Karl T. Compton, was quoted in the same year as saying "he did not believe Russia had the atomic bomb or would have it in the near future." Another physicist, Ralph Lapp, who had been intimately involved with the development of America's atomic bomb, and who later served as executive secretary of the Atomic Energy Committee of the Defense Department's Research and Development Board, made a prediction similar to Compton's in 1949. "It seems reasonable to assume," Lapp wrote in a book called *Must We Hide?*, "that other nations will not develop bombs until 1952. . . ." American scientists were not the only ones who were so wide of the mark. An English physicist, M. L. Oliphant, was quoted in *The New York Times* of March 29, 1948, as saying, "Those of us taking part in the atomic energy project do not believe that within the

Russian sphere there can be sufficient knowledge or specialized skill to build a successful plant for many years to come." Wohlstetter also points out that many scientists have overestimated the speed with which nuclear weapons would be acquired by countries other than the great powers. In 1960, for example, C. P. Snow told the American Association for the Advancement of Science that "all physical scientists . . . *know* that for a dozen or more states, it will only take perhaps six years, perhaps less, to acquire fission and fusion bombs."[13]

Scientists who believe they have the future in their bones are also inclined to attribute the ills of the world to the muddleheadedness of politicians and diplomats, and to suppose that these ills could be cured if "policy [were] made primarily by forward-looking, solution-oriented, rational-thinking types" like themselves.*[14] This can have several unfortunate consequences. It can lead to the proposal of solutions to world problems that do not allow for the fact that people, as well as politicians, behave in selfish and irrational ways. It can also lead a scientist who has proposed a solution to a problem, and had his advice rejected or ignored, to conclude that politicians and policymakers are beyond salvation, and to wash his hands of them—instead of trying to modify his proposal to improve its chances of being accepted.

Finally, a scientist's belief in his superior rationality may persuade him—and other people—that his views on how to stop wars, or how to deal with China, should carry extra weight simply because they are put forward by a scientist.

---

* This view, of course, is seldom put so baldly. But it is clearly reflected, for example, in the following comment made by the astronomer Harlow Shapley in 1957 at the time of the International Geophysical Year. "All goes smoothly," he wrote. "We in IGY cooperate; in the UN they expostulate. The musicians are doing a little also, and the cardiologists; student exchanges should increase. . . . I pause here a second to exclaim, uselessly, 'curses on the diplomats.' Useless—but it gives me a bit of relief."[15]

This assumes that any good scientist would hold similar views—a claim that is very hard to sustain in the face of the bitter arguments American scientists have had over such matters as the desirability of pressing ahead with the hydrogen bomb, or the terms the United States should insist on before signing a nuclear test-ban treaty with Russia. In the case of the test-ban treaty, it is clear in retrospect that the opposing factions were pretty much in agreement about the technical strengths and weaknesses of various systems for detecting treaty violations. What they disagreed about were such things as whether the Russians would try to cheat (and, if so, how hard they would try), and whether the United States or the Soviet Union stood to lose more, from a military standpoint, if testing were stopped—questions to which there are, of course, no "scientific" answers.

Scientists who have begun their careers since World War Two seem less inclined to feel they are specially qualified to lead mankind out of darkness and error. They may sign statements opposing the bombing of North Vietnam, or calling for the early conclusion of a treaty to limit the spread of nuclear weapons, but they sign as professors, or intellectuals, or liberals, or internationalists, rather than as scientists. Many younger men who spend a good deal of time as government consultants draw the line at giving anything but technical advice. "I believe in some abstract way that physicists are very smart," a member of the Jason group told me. "As a group, they are probably smarter than any other group of people in the country. Most of them have the capacity to be bright about certain types of problems—engineering problems, for instance. But I don't know if being a physicist helps in solving political problems. I personally would be uncomfortable giving political advice."

But scientists continue to deliver offhand opinions on

nontechnical matters, often with great confidence and in circumstances that may lead the unwary to suppose that they are speaking *ex cathedra*. In 1963, for instance, the distinguished chemist Harold C. Urey was invited by the Senate Committee on Aeronautical and Space Sciences to give his views on the value of trying to put a man on the moon by 1970. Urey said modestly that "the reasons for the speed [of the moon race] lie outside the range of scientific considerations, and I think perhaps I am not in a good position to judge them." Despite this disclaimer, however, Urey went on to say why he thought the man-on-the-moon program was going ahead at just about the right speed. "The industrial companies, the scientists, the engineers, and the administrators cannot be attracted to this work unless some certain rate of accomplishment rewards them for the work," he testified. He also told the committee that the real reason for the space program is to be found in "an innate characteristic of human beings, namely some curious drive to do what might be thought impossible . . ."[16]

Urey may have been right. But his views seem to have been no more solidly grounded than those of, say, a reasonably intelligent stock broker holding forth on the space race on the 5:03 to Greenwich. Amitai Etzioni, a sociologist and the author of *The Moon-doggle: Domestic and International Implications of the Space Race*, has noted that "industrial economists do not consider the pace of 'accomplishment' as important as Dr. Urey indicates. They are more interested in the rate of profit, which attracts industries to the competition for a place in space—a profit that can be kept quite high, even if the space race is slowed down by half. As for 'innate characteristics,' psychologists gave up the search for them long ago and no one has yet discovered a drive to do the impossible on space or on earth." Etzioni adds drily, "It is somewhat difficult to believe that we came under the spell of this universal drive precisely on October 5, 1957—before the Russians orbited Sputnik our drive to explore space was quite controlled."[17]

This sort of thing tends to undermine the authority and credibility of scientists, and these are further undermined when scientists assume, as they often do, that they are immune to the bias of self-interest. Another witness before the Aeronautics and Space Committee, Colin S. Pittendrigh, an eminent Princeton biologist, began by observing that he was in favor of the man-on-the-moon program. He went on to say, "I have no vested interest in the space program, in the sense that the main line of my professional work will be very little affected by how this program develops." The following colloquy then took place:

The Chairman (Senator Clinton P. Anderson): "Doctor, I will have to stop you just for a second because I read a newspaper story—I do not remember who wrote it—saying that of the ten scientists who will testify, all but one have a direct financial interest in the program. Do you have a direct financial interest in the space program?"

Dr. Pittendrigh: "I am not quite sure what financial means in this context. I do not own shares in an aircraft company, no."

The Chairman: "Well, the reporter says that most of you do have."

Dr. Pittendrigh: "I really do not understand."

The director of the Committee staff intervened at this point to explain the Chairman's question:

Mr. Di Luzio: "Government contracts with yourself personally or the institution with which you are associated."

Dr. Pittendrigh: "Oh, yes, indeed, I do receive funds from the Space Administration for part of my work, that is true."[18]

There is nothing to suggest that Pittendrigh or any of the other witnesses were consciously trying to ingratiate themselves with the people in charge of the money at NASA. But two facts that came out at the hearing do suggest that scientists may be less free from unconscious bias than they may like to think. One fact is that the scientists who testified most enthusiastically in favor of the moon program were in almost every case either getting research funds from NASA, or had colleagues who were. The other fact was supplied by Philip Abelson. An uninhibited critic of the program, Abelson told the committee that he had taken an informal straw poll among scientists "not connected by self-interest to NASA," and that "the vote was 110 to 3 against the present manned lunar program."[19]

It would be foolish for the government to bar as advisers all scientists benefiting in any way from the programs about which their advice might be asked. Often this would mean ruling out all the leading people in a given field of research. But there could be a rule requiring agencies to disclose all connections, direct and indirect, linking their scientific advisers with programs that the agency administers. As it is, the public often has no way of knowing even the names of scientists on whom the government is calling for advice. Appointments to P-SAC are a matter of public record, but the names of scientists serving on P-SAC study panels usually are not. The identities of scientists serving many other advisory panels, including the Jason group, are also kept secret—presumably on the theory that advice from scientists is so objective that it doesn't matter which particular scientists are giving it. This policy not only keeps the public from knowing whose scientific advice the government is following (or ignoring), but probably tends to encourage sloppy work on the part of advisers. Ironically, as Meg Greenfield, Washington correspondent of *The Reporter*, has noted, the possibility that such work may occur has been cited as justification for the policy that permits it. "The point, as it is often argued in Washington," Miss Greenfield writes, "is that government simply could not get scientists to come down to perfunctory, accident-prone, potentially embarrassing work if even so much as their identity were revealed."[20]

Requiring government agencies to disclose the names and connections of all scientific consultants might jack up the standards of advice-giving. But it would do little or nothing to help political leaders decide what weight they should give to the recommendations of their scientific advisers—a problem that arises in a particularly troubling form when the advisers disagree. It has been suggested that the solution is for scientists to distinguish clearly between their scientific opinions and opinions that are shaped by their general views of man and society. Scientists should, of course, try to do this, and those who don't make the effort are much more likely than in the past to be questioned sharply by their clients. But to suppose that scientists can always make this separation, particularly when they are dealing with matters like disarmament, or nuclear testing, or the use of pesticides, on which passions run high in the scientific community, is to fall into much the same error of which Snow is guilty—that is, to assume that scientists are supermen.

It is much more sensible to take for granted that political biases or, to put it more positively, political values will inevitably affect at times the advice given by scientists, and to allow for this by including on all important scientific advisory bodies, other than those that deal with purely technical questions, scientists with opposing outlooks. The result, Robert Gilpin writes in *American Scientists and Nuclear Weapons Policy*, would be "to raise to a conscious level the implicit non-technical assumptions which frequently cause apparent scientific disagreement, while leaving intact the points of scientific agreement."[21] As Gilpin suggests elsewhere in his book, things may not always work out so tidily. But confrontations of the kind he endorses can at least alert the President, his Cabinet members, and the Congress to the possibility that what they are being offered as "scientific" advice is not scientific at all.

To deny that scientists are "specially endowed to bring order and sense to the political process" is not to say that they should have no place in politics or public affairs. With American science so dependent on federal bounty, it is in everybody's interest that scientists have a great deal to say about who receives this bounty and the terms on which it is given out. The advice of scientists is also indispensable to the government in arriving at decisions that turn largely on technological considerations—on whether, for example, a proposed system of air-traffic control is technically feasible, and what it might cost as compared with alternative systems. In the military sphere, questions of this kind now are often dealt with in a more or less routine fashion by full-time professionals, trained in strategic or systems analysis, who work for the Defense Department or for a satellite research organization like the RAND Corporation or the Institute for Defense Analyses. But the Defense Department still calls on leading academic scientists for help in solving scientific and technological problems that are outside the sector patrolled by the so-called defense intellectuals. And in other areas of government, the advice of scientists will be sought whenever the possibility exists that technological problems blocking a particular course of action might be solved if they were reformulated in radically different terms.

Besides helping to design and operate the machinery by which science is supported, and besides suggesting ways of solving or getting around difficult technical problems that the government may face, scientists can play another important part in public affairs. Scientists are no more (and no less) obligated than anyone else to sign statements about the war in Vietnam, or the draft, or relations with China. But they perhaps have a special responsibility to speak out about the social implications, both good and bad, of their own and other scientists' research—and, in addition, to raise the alarm when applications that are being made of scientific discoveries seem likely to have dangerous consequences. In the 1950's, for instance, scientists, including some who were consultants to the Atomic Energy Commission, were successful in persuading Americans that the AEC was seriously understating the dangers of radioactive fallout from atomic weapons. Researchers are not the only people who can grasp the implications of their research, and of its applications. But businessmen, military leaders, and other people engaged in exploiting scientific discoveries cannot be counted on for objective appraisals of the possible damage they may be doing. To rely on drug manufacturers to publicize the danger, or the foolishness, of excessive use of certain classes of drugs (tranquilizers, for instance) would be a little like relying on logging companies to protect the country's forests.

In any case, scientists are likely to be among the first to realize the legal, ethical, and other problems that may arise as a result of the application of their own findings. This is particularly true when scientific discoveries open the way for radical changes of an unprecedented kind in the conditions of human existence—changes such as will occur, for example, when techniques are developed for controlling genetically determined characteristics of human beings. In this sense, scientists do have the future in their bones; and they would seem to owe it to their fellow men to consider carefully what their bones tell them, and to pass the message on.

X

Eden After Twenty Years

F OR ANY AMERICAN who has a taste, and at least a modest aptitude, for basic scientific investigation, this is a Golden Age. He may choose to spend part of his time teaching or, like a feudal nobleman, claim exemption from all useful toil. If, from time to time, he deigns to turn his attention to practical affairs, he does so for relaxation or profit, or from a sense of noblesse oblige, not because he has to. In a society where so many men despise their work, or despise themselves for doing it, the basic researcher is free to do pretty much what he likes with his time. He makes a good living into the bargain.

Many scientists take these privileges happily for granted. But anyone who undertakes to portray scientific life in America today must in the end account not only for its confidence and euphoria, but for certain currents of apprehension and guilt that flow just beneath its surface. The source of this uneasiness, like the source of the euphoria, is the prosperity that scientists now enjoy. Some scientists are troubled by the magnitude of the sums that are now being spent for basic research. Others are troubled not by the amount of money that is being spent, but by the

254

ambiguity of the terms on which scientists, as a group, have solicited and accepted it.

The view that science is being too richly nourished for its own good has been put forward by, among others, the distinguished American biologist Paul A. Weiss. In an address given at the University and Academy of Padua in 1961, Weiss complained that while the achievements of contemporary biology were undeniably superb, the average quality of biological research had been falling off badly. "The symptoms are many," he said. "We see instruments turning from servants into tyrants, forcing the captive scientist to mass-produce and market senseless data beyond the point of conceivable usefulness—a modern version of the Sorcerer's Apprentice. We see bewildered youngsters composing research projects like abstract paintings: picking some colorful and fashionable words from recent literature, and then reshuffling and recombining them into another conglomerate, yielding a stew of data, both undigested and indigestible. We see narrow specialists lavishing their pet technique on reconfirming in yet another dozen ways what has already been superabundantly established to everybody's satisfaction. But why go on? Most of you will know the hallmarks of this growing dilution of research effectiveness. They are irrelevance, triviality, redundancy, lack of perspective, and unbounded flair for proliferation."[1] Most of the scientists interviewed by Bernice Eiduson in 1964 held similar opinions. "The majority . . . noticed a deterioration in research quality," she writes. "They point out that more 'hacks' have been drawn into the field. . . . As one physicist said, 'These hacks flock like locusts to well-funded areas and bring into science a level of ordinariness which previously would not have been tolerated."[2]

There is no reason to question the validity of these complaints. If government and private subsidies were to bring about a rapid four- or five-fold increase in the number of professional poets and painters in the United States, one would not expect a four- or five-fold increase in the number of good poems and good paintings. The situation in science is pretty much the same. Derek de Solla Price has, in fact, ingeniously demonstrated that while the number of scientists in the world has doubled every ten to fifteen years for the past three hundred years, the number of brilliant and productive scientists has increased at a much slower rate. According to Price's calculations, the number of good scientists increases only as the square root of the increase in the total number of scientists; that is, when the scientific population quadruples, the number of good scientists only doubles.[3]

Scientists are inclined to blame the decline in the average quality of scientific work partly on the fact that, as they see it, far too many people are now becoming scientists for the wrong reasons. Until quite recently, Weiss noted in his remarks at Padua, "to be a scientist was a calling, not a job." He went on to say, "Scientists were men of science, not just men in science. They had come to science driven by an inner urge, curiosity, a quest for knowledge. . . . They were not drawn or lured into science in masses by fascinating gadgets, public acclaim, manpower needs of industries and government, or job security; nor did they just drift in for no good reason. The scene, however, is now changing rapidly. The popularity and needs of an expanding science bring in more drifters and followers than pioneers."

One should not, perhaps, take these remarks at face value. Older men—Weiss was born in 1898—have always been inclined to recall how hard they worked when they were young, and how idealistic they were, and to complain that the younger generation is going to the dogs. Long before scientific careers were fashionable, men became scientists for reasons other than a passionate determination to discover and reveal the truth about the universe. Einstein, in a passage from which I have already quoted, once remarked that in addition to those men who regarded science as a kind of sport, there were scientists "who come into the temple [of science] to make an offering of their brain pulp in the hope of securing a profitable return." These men, he said, "are scientists only by chance of circumstance which offered itself when making a choice of career. If the attending circumstances had been different they might have become politicians or captains of business. Should an angel of God descend and drive from the temple of Science all those who belong to the categories I have mentioned, I fear the temple would be nearly emptied."[4]

It seems very likely, however, that the number of people who become scientists because science offers a good living has been increasing much faster than the number of people who become scientists because they can't conceive of becoming anything else. Louise Elizabeth Merz, a sociologist, reported after interviewing a group of graduate students in the physics and chemistry departments of a big eastern university that almost all the chemists in her sample were "job-oriented"; that is, they said they were at graduate school because they wanted to qualify themselves for better-paying jobs. One student, an organic chemist, told her, "Although I now say that a professional, even one in industry, should consider whether the problem will make a contribution to his field in deciding to work on it, when I get into industry I'm going to change my point of view. Industry says that you have to worry about whether the problem is going to make money for them. And when I get there I am going to subscribe one hundred percent to their way of thinking." It is most improbable that a similar survey made forty years ago, when industry was just beginning to hire large numbers of chemists with advanced degrees, would have revealed so many job-oriented chemists as Miss Merz found. Certainly it would not have turned up any physics students like the one who told her, "I don't know about all this romanticizing of physics. As far as I am concerned, physics is no different from any other occupation. It is work. Like every other kind of work, it's a job. I'm interested in it because it so happens you can get very good jobs in physics that pay a lot of money, as long as you have a Ph.D. So that's why I decided to come to graduate school."[5]

Why should anyone object to people taking up scientific careers because they are looking for good pay and job security? Their doing so does not prevent other people from going into science for reasons of which Weiss would heartily approve. Most of the first-year graduate students in physics whom Miss Merz interviewed were classified by her as "field-oriented," meaning that they talked and acted as if they looked on science as an end in itself. (One student said, "Well, as a sophomore in college I got to be interested in physics, what was going on there. And I became so intrigued with physics that there was no stopping me. I developed a voracious appetite for it. . . . I got so that the only thing of concern was pursuing physical truth, put that in quotes, in any way that I could. It's physics that matters to me."[6]) Furthermore, very useful work can be done by scientists who can take science or leave it alone. This is particularly true in applied science, and in certain kinds of basic research, such as high-energy physics, in which investigations have to be carried out by large teams. Even in basic research that can be carried out by individuals or small groups journeyman scientists may contribute indirectly to important discoveries. A series of tedious and intrinsically boring experiments may, for example, disclose discrepancies that are not accounted for by existing theory, and thereby inspire the formulation of a new and better theory. The value of such experiments, which may consist of making very precise measurements, has been acknowledged by, among others, the physicist Hans Bethe. In 1962 Bethe remarked to an interviewer that the huge sums of money that had been spent for physical research over the preceding thirty years had yielded nothing comparable to the theory of relativity or the quantum theory—only "a lot of detail—important, but nothing that you cannot summarize in one or two sentences." Yet when he was asked if all these details were needed to permit significant new advances, he answered, "Probably not 'all,' but we don't know which are going to be important."[7]

The reason scientists commonly give for feeling alarmed by the proliferation of trivial and redundant research was stated in these terms by the late Norbert Wiener: "[S]uppose you have a mass of low-grade scientific work. If it is your duty to look through it all in order to find the high-grade scientific work, the mass of it makes finding the high-grade scientific work much more difficult. . . . The existence of the other work doesn't help you find the really fundamental scientific work one bit. It makes this a harder task."[8]

But it is doubtful whether the difficulty that Wiener describes is as serious as scientists sometimes claim. Spectacular advances have been made in biology in recent decades despite the fact that as far back as 1905, if one may credit a speech made in that year by Dean Andrew Fleming West of Princeton, "the flood of publications, say in some subsection of the vast field of biology, is swamping men."[9] Furthermore, scientists who complain about the number of unimportant research papers that are being cranked out seldom say that this has had any effect on their own work. Thus although Dr. Eiduson's scientists agreed that the average quality of research in their fields

had been declining, "the majority . . . could cite no negative effects of the heavy government subsidy on the creativity of the individual scientist."[10] As a matter of fact,
active and successful researchers often spend very little
time reading scientific journals. As I have pointed out, they
are likely to belong to invisible colleges made up of the
leading people in their field. The members of such colleges
not only meet one another periodically at summer institutes and colloquia, but they keep each other posted on
what they are doing by exchanging pre-prints of articles
they plan to publish. They assume that if anyone outside
their circle does something interesting they will learn of it
quickly enough by word of mouth.

One scientist with whom I spoke, a neurochemist, did
say that he felt overwhelmed by the amount of reading he
has to do. Like many scientists in certain branches of
biomedical research (and in many kinds of applied research), he needs to keep up with what people are doing in
a number of fields and disciplines besides his own. "I can't
look at a piece of brain tissue without considering what
people in electron microscopy see when *they* look at it," he
said. "This is only one example. You get worried that
you're going to miss an important observation that will
lead you forward with your own work. I spend more and
more time reading, or searching, the literature. Even so, I
miss things. I know I've missed them when I submit a
paper to a journal, and the referee says, 'You didn't refer to
so-and-so.' " This scientist said he would not be in favor,
however, of cutting down on the number of papers that are
published. "You can't be omniscient about these things," he
said. "Something that doesn't seem pertinent to anything at
the moment may prove later to be of great value."

There are other, and deeper, reasons why many scientists, particularly if they are middle-aged or older, are

dismayed by the rate at which the number of basic researchers has been growing. It is characteristic of the way science develops that when an important new discovery is made, workers will rush in to exploit it. To the discoverer, this is gratifying proof of the significance of his discovery. But it can also be depressing when, as is now often the case, the rush is massive and almost instantaneous. Today the scientist who opens up a new field very quickly finds himself hemmed in, as it were, by settlers who cut down the trees, plow up the land, and kill off all the game. He must either pull up stakes and move on, or else resign himself not only to watching the forests give way to field but to watching the fields fill up with ranch and split-level houses.

Yet even though few scientists in the future are likely to know the feeling of spaciousness and leisure that physicists enjoyed at Göttingen and Copenhagen in the 1920's there is little chance that this will keep young people from going into science. At twenty, one does not think very much about the kind of life one will be leading at forty or forty-five. And, in any case, the fact that science is no longer the property of a happy few will not discourage the best people, who characteristically are already so caught up in science by the time they are twenty that they cannot imagine being anything else but a scientist. "Anyone who is really hooked on research is willing to live with the unpleasant aspects of the game as it is presently played," a young biophysicist wrote me. "He doesn't give it up for a career in college teaching or elsewhere. Rather, he tries to mitigate the unpleasant aspects—sometimes by teaching—and carries on."

The uneasiness that many scientists feel when they contemplate the growing mass of researchers who think of research as a good job (or as a stepping-stone on the way to a better one) also reflects a fear that bad or mediocre science will drive out good science. "Science has to be run by and for the competent, plodding people who make up the vast majority of scientists today," I was told by a young microbiologist. "It can't be run for geniuses, for the people who break through into new territory. They tend to be selfish and anarchistic, whereas the general tone of science is solid, social, conservative, and hierarchical." At present, geniuses make out very well. The scientist whom I have just quoted, for example, is selfish and anarchistic, and yet he has all the support he needs to do exactly what he wants in the way of research. But there is a danger, as I have suggested in connection with Big Science, that scientific affairs will increasingly be run by scientists who attach so much importance to tidiness and order and detailed plans that the anarchistic and unbusinesslike physicist or biologist will have a hard time getting support. The result may be to drive gifted anarchists into fields where research is relatively cheap, and where they will not have to ask for big grants or compete for the use of expensive research facilities.

As I have said, American scientists are often troubled—and should perhaps be more troubled than they are—by a certain ambiguity in the terms on which they have obtained their extraordinary privileges. In a country that not long ago thought of basic scientific research as an arcane hobby, the government now gives large numbers of scientists the time and means to gratify their curiosity about the natural world, exacting in return no more than that a man's work be interesting to other scientists who are doing the same sort of work as he is.

Many scientists feel no other justification should be required. They argue that science should be thought of not as a means to a useful end, but as an end in itself, like art and literature and music. Some scientists go so far as to assert that science is the supreme expression of the human spirit. "The arts are certainly central to life," the physicist I. I. Rabi has said. "Yet they are not the kind of thing that will inspire men to push on to new heights. Suppose we were to become a nation of poets and were taught in school, as the Japanese are taught, that every good citizen should write a poem. Some would be very good and people would read and enjoy them. But what would anybody talk about? Only everyday things—love, sorrow, life, and death. If men want to go beyond these everyday things to a grand theme, they will find it only in science." Rabi then explains that art and literature are not in the same realm of originality as science, and that even the works of Shakespeare "are really wonderful, glorified gossip. I mean, after Shakespeare and others, how many more persons can say the same things?" he asks. "They can say it in different ways, they can say it in beautiful ways and in other contexts, and I hope they will never stop. But just the same, where do we find the really new thing, the moving thing, the thing that will show the glory of God and the originality of nature, the profundity—and where do we find the imagination that delves into the mysteries of life, into the existence of matter? That imagination, I would say, will be found only in science."[11]

While Rabi's remarks would rightly strike many scientists as arrogant or naïve, few people would deny that scientific inquiry and speculation have an intrinsic value that has nothing to do with any practical benefits that may flow from them. Moreover, it can be argued that even if science had no practical uses at all, it would have a better claim on the patronage of the state than art or literature or music. For one thing, a basic researcher differs from a novelist or sculptor in that he cannot sell the product of his labors. For another, scientific research is usually a lot more expensive than painting a picture or writing a poem. The quality of American painting and poetry would suffer very little if all government subsidies were to be cut off, and it would improve very little even if American poets and painters were to get ten times as much money from the government as they now get. By contrast, if the government were to cut back drastically on the money it is putting into basic research, a good many of the country's best scientists would have to drop what they are doing, and some would doubtless move to other countries.

Governments do not, of course, support basic scientific research simply because it is an intellectually invigorating enterprise that can thrive only if nourished by public subsidies. It is also assumed that scientists, in the course of exploring nature, will inevitably make discoveries that can be converted into power—power to create wealth, ease labor, cure disease, and wage war. A corollary of this irrefutable proposition is that a thousand dollars spent on free scientific inquiry may in the end yield bigger technological dividends than a million dollars spent prematurely on applied research. No amount of money spent on applied research could have procured the formulation of those fundamental laws of matter and energy whose discovery made possible the invention of radio and television and the atomic bomb. Like a businessman operating in the kind of market described by Adam Smith, the scientist can argue that in pursuing his own selfish (and purely scientific) ends, he is making his greatest contribution to the wealth and well being of his fellow men.

Other things being equal, many scientists would rather not make this argument. They would like to be cherished for the elegance and virtuosity of their intellectual constructions, not for their usefulness. But if American scientists had argued in the 1940's that the government should invest in pure science because science is beautiful and exciting, they would not have had much of a hearing. As it was, the bombing of Hiroshima and Nagasaki had given the world a striking and terrible lesson in the power of pure science to change the conditions of human existence, and the fact that the United States government is now spending over two billion dollars a year on basic research is a measure of how well American scientists have driven this lesson home. "In a way we are all getting money under false pretenses," I was told by a physicist who was helping to build and put into operation the new linear accelerator at Stanford. Sitting on the balcony outside his handsome office, which overlooks one end of the two-mile-long accelerator tunnel, he said, "You know, we go to Congress and we say, 'This is pure science. It has no practical applications that anyone can foresee. Exploring the atomic nucleus is pure intellectual adventure.' The congressmen nod. They say, 'Yes, that's fine.' But they're really thinking about Einstein, and E equals MC squared, and about the possibility that somehow some new superweapon might come of this. And way down deep inside we know that's what they're thinking. Of course we take the money anyway."

The trouble with the Faustian bargain to which American scientists have been a willing party is that sooner or later the devil will demand his due. The time may now be at hand. The expectations that were aroused in 1945, when it appeared that if scientists could invent an atom bomb they could invent anything, have not been realized. New products—plastics, artificial fibres, transistors, antibiotics, computers, color television sets—have, to be sure, flowed in a generous stream from the springs of scientific knowledge, and scientists whose main concern is with pure research have had a great deal to do with the development of new and more potent weapons. But science has done little or nothing to mitigate hunger, poverty, inequality, ignorance, or even to improve the quality of housing, urban transportation, and medical services.

As a result, while everyone agrees that basic research, like religion and regular physical exercise, should be encouraged, politicians are beginning to ask when and how the government is going to get its money back. The questioners include President Johnson, who told a group of medical leaders in 1966 that the government should begin putting more emphasis on applied medical research. "I think the time has now come to zero in on the targets by trying to get our knowledge fully applied," he said. "There are hundreds of millions of dollars spent on laboratory research that may be useful to human beings if large-scale trials on patients are initiated in programming areas."[12] The President later took occasion to make it clear that the government is firmly committed to basic biomedical research "because we believe that all knowledge is precious; because we know that all progress would halt without it."[13] But at a time when the cost of doing research, and the number of people who are qualified to do it, are both rising, the amount of money the government is investing in basic research is scarcely rising at all.

Leaders of the American scientific establishment, bearing down hard on the fable of the goose that laid the golden eggs, have generally responded by arguing that while applied research may well need a shot in the arm, an injection of funds taken out of the basic-research budget would not really help matters. Actually, the main effect of such a transfer of funds might be to place a premium on slickness and adroit salesmanship in the competition for research grants. As Harvey Brooks of Harvard, who is himself an applied scientist, recently warned, "The availability of large resources for efforts of apparent social importance may tempt scientists to make expedient promises of quick utility in order to obtain support for work they wish to undertake." Brooks noted that "the unfortunate aspect of this is that, usually, the less the ability and integrity of the scientist, the more willing he is to invent expedient labels for his work, so that the net effect of providing support preferentially for fields or projects that have the appearance of immediate social utility is to drive the best and most creative minds out of the field."[14]

The ablest young scientists have very good reasons for avoiding careers in applied science. As a basic researcher, a man can be his own boss. He is, of course, subject to the pressures of the market in which he offers his wares. But the values of this market are *his* values, while the problems on which an applied scientist works are usually chosen for him by other people, who may not be scientists, and whose values in any case may be quite different from his. A scientist who runs a division of a government or industrial laboratory cannot decide for himself whether to undertake a research program aimed at developing a new nerve gas, or a slightly different version of a best-selling antibiotic. Like any other manager, his job is to carry out the policies his superiors have decided on, even if these policies are directed toward ends that he considers trivial or even antisocial.

Bright young scientists also tend to avoid applied science simply because it is unfashionable. Brooks, in the paper from which I have already quoted, points out that while "a certain snobbery has always existed between pure and applied science," there were at one time powerful forces pulling young scientists away from pure research. Once, he writes, "the exponents of pure science represented a small and rather ascetic minority who took pride in sacrificing the greater material rewards of applied science for what were thought of as the greater psychological satisfactions of pure science. . . ." Today, by contrast, "the

gaps in both material reward and external prestige between basic and applied science have largely disappeared."
Middle-class Americans, moved perhaps by a wish to live
down a reputation for crass materialism, more and more
often are to be found worshiping at the altar of nonutility.
As Brooks observes, "The business tycoon . . . boasts of his
son's achievements as a theoretical physicist or a Sanskrit
scholar."[15]

The snobbery of the pure scientist once had a certain
point. It served to arm him, and his disciples, against the
temptations of more worldly and better-paying occupations. But no useful purpose is now served by telling young
scientists that applied research is only for dullards. By
keeping able men from trying their hands at organizing
and running applied-research programs, even under the
most favorable auspices, such indoctrination becomes a
self-fulfilling prophecy. Its harmful effect on certain kinds
of biomedical research has recently been emphasized by
an advisory committee that looked into the administration
of research programs sponsored by the National Institutes
of Health. The committee found that "the most crucial
single problem to be faced at NIH is the scarcity of individuals in the biomedical area with the technical background, experience, and temperament needed to assume the
responsibilities of program management." This is largely
due, the committee said, to "the extreme reluctance of
biomedical scientists to engage in administration or management of any type, much less the management of directed research on a full-time basis. Traditionally, the
biochemical scientist has regarded his proper role in Government as that of advisor rather than responsible manager,
and this tradition will not be altered easily. . . . The biomedical administrator or manager, at present, lacks status
in the eyes of his peers."[16]

A scientist may argue that this is all too bad, but that

putting science to practical use is not his job. Even from a purely selfish standpoint, however, this makes little sense. Basic researchers in the United States are supported largely by tax money, and the taxpayers' representatives have been taught by scientists themselves that basic research is not really useless—that it differs from applied research mainly in that it doesn't pay off quite so quickly. In the long run, the patrons of basic research will judge it by its utility. Unless new scientific knowledge is more efficiently and imaginatively transmuted into social benefits, the public may easily become disenchanted with pure science, and put basic researchers on much shorter rations than they have grown accustomed to.

Inducing a larger proportion of the less talented scientists to labor in the vineyards of applied science will do little good. Nor will the establishment of more summer study groups in which academic scientists can address themselves to technological problems on a part-time basis. The trouble with applied research in the United States is not only, as I have suggested, that able scientists tend to turn their noses up at it. The main trouble is that the conditions under which applied scientists have to work in government and industry are often frustrating and sometimes degrading. If science is to be used more efficiently, ways must be found of preserving in large-scale applied research some of the autonomy and free cooperation that characterize basic research.

This point has been made by, among others, Albert B. Sabin, whose work was largely responsible for the development of live-virus polio vaccine. There are important questions in the biomedical sciences, Sabin recently told a Senate committee, that can be solved only by the coordinated efforts of many people. The success of such efforts, he said, will depend on the willingness of good scientists to take part in them, "and this in turn will depend on the extent to which they can participate in the original planning and critique of the total research plan and on the extent to which opportunities for individual initiative and ingenuity remain in the cooperative enterprise." Sabin emphasized the importance of placing the main responsibility for managing such programs in the hands of the scientists who have conceived them. Their responsibilities, he said, should include "assignment of funds to participants; selection of participants and new recruits . . . frequent discussions of results in progress; and cooperative modification of the total research plan as new situations arise."[17]

There are a few government and industrial laboratories where scientists now have a great deal of freedom both in choosing technological goals and in deciding on the best means of attaining them. But if American scientists are to square their accounts with their patrons, they will have to help in devising institutional arrangements that will encourage free cooperation in the application of science to useful ends. One need not agree with Bacon that "Knowledge, that tendeth but to satisfaction is but as a courtesan, which is for pleasure, and not for fruit or generation." In an ideal society, in which all material wants were satisfied, it is clear that the pursuit of knowledge for its own sake would be one of the main objects of life. But we live in a world in which hundreds of millions of people are poor, hungry, diseased, ignorant, and exploited by their fellow men, and in which scientists may have it in their power to help alleviate misery and despair. It would not only be shortsighted, but immoral, if all scientists who could contrive to do so were to withhold their help on the ground that they owed their allegiance not to utility, but to truth.

This is not to say that "pure" science would be morally justified only in a perfect world. Even in an imperfect one, gifted men with a passion for science should be encouraged to gratify it without having to pay for the privilege by performing useful works. The question is, how gifted must a scientist be in order to deserve this status? Many very talented scientists do, in fact, spend a great deal of their time wrestling with practical problems, or using their special knowledge and skills in the service of causes such as disarmament, conservation, and population control. But science in America would probably be healthier, and scientists would have less reason to feel uneasy about their privileged position, if scientists of first-rate abilities were to accept more responsibility for the quality of applied research. To discharge this responsibility, they will have to dirty their hands with the grubby work of building, and actually operating, better social machinery for extracting useful benefits from science.

Appendix

Why Social Scientists
Don't Fit In

SOCIAL SCIENTISTS, by which I mean all psychologists, as well as economists, sociologists, anthropologists, and political scientists, are coming more and more to resemble natural scientists. They collect and analyze enormous quantities of data, make experiments, use computers, build mathematical models, and formulate general laws—in their case, laws intended to explain the behavior of men and institutions. They also do a great deal of applied research for clients both in and out of government. But despite these similarities, social scientists still differ from physicists and chemists and biologists in a number of significant ways. For example:

Social scientists disagree violently about what they should be doing, and how they should be doing it. Sects and schools and ideological schisms are far more common in the social than in the natural sciences. If you ask a random selection of high-energy physicists to name the best people in their field, their answers will tend to agree, whereas in sociology, for instance, you will get one list if you ask an admirer of the late C. Wright Mills, and another if you ask a disciple of Talcott Parsons. One major disagreement is over the question of how "scientific" the social sciences should be. In *The Effects of Federal Programs on Higher Education*, Harold Orlans remarks that in the social sciences "federal programs have tended to support quantitative, statistical, and either real or mock experimental approaches which—partly for this reason, it may be argued—are more dominant than they were several decades ago."[1] Some social scientists think this is a good thing, and that real progress in fields like psychology and sociology will come only through greater reliance on mathematical techniques. Others argue that quantitative studies have become fashionable not because they yield important new knowledge about behavior, but simply because it is easier to get money for work that has a comforting appearance of scientific solidity.

In the scientific community, social scientists generally have to live on the wrong side of the tracks. With the exception of psychologists, they have a much harder time than natural scientists do in getting research grants. In 1960–61, at twelve large universities surveyed by Orlans, only one out of three sociologists and anthropologists, one out of five economists, and one out of fourteen political scientists got any support from the federal government for their research. By contrast, half of the psychologists at the same universities, and three-quarters of all the natural scientists, had government support.[2] (Since 1960, government outlays for social research have more than quadrupled, but most of the money is going into applied research, and social scientists who want support for fundamental studies are still at a big disadvantage.)

Social scientists also have a hard time getting into the best clubs, so to speak. Although a political scientist, Don K. Price, was elected president for 1967 of the American Association for the Advancement of Science, there are no political scientists in the National Academy of Sciences. Nor are there any sociologists or economists. The Academy does from time to time take in psychologists and anthropologists, but in a total membership of 740 there are only 27 of the former and 18 of the latter. As of mid-1967, moreover, there were no social scientists on the President's Science Advisory Committee. Commenting on this fact, one committee member, William R. Hewlett, an engineer and manufacturer, recently observed that "this field [the social sciences] lacks the specifics characteristic of the physical sciences and thus provides a greater opportunity for strongly divergent views on technical subjects," and that consequently it would not be enough to have just one social scientist on the committee. "Each discussion that I have heard," he added loftily, "has resulted in the consensus that it would not be profitable to dilute P-SAC's limited manpower with two or more social scientists at a time when there are so many unsolved problems in the field of the physical sciences."*[3]

As a class, social scientists do not wield the same magical power that natural scientists wield. A few social scientists, of whom Marx and Freud are the most striking examples, have had a profound influence on the way men look at themselves and at one another, and on the evolution of human institutions. But considered either as a body of knowledge, or as a set of methods for investigating certain aspects of reality, the social sciences have not had anything like the impact on human life that the natural sciences have. They have given birth to such technological offspring as public opinion polls and intelligence tests, but nothing that is comparable to antibiotics or atom bombs.

It can also be argued that pointless and pedestrian research is a good deal more prevalent in the social than in the natural sciences. At any rate, it can be spotted more easily by laymen. Barrington Moore, a professor of political sociology at Harvard, cites, for example, a study of

* Since this was written, a social scientist has at last made the team. He is Herbert A. Simon, professor of industrial administration and psychology at Carnegie-Mellon University, who was appointed to P-SAC in February, 1968.

"Male Sex Aggression on a University Campus," from which one learns that: "Of the 291 responding girls 55.7 per cent reported themselves offended at least once during the academic year at some level of erotic intimacy. The experiences of being offended were not altogether associated with trivial situations as shown by the fact that 20.9 per cent were offended by forceful attempts at intercourse and 6.2 per cent by 'aggressively forceful attempt at sex intercourse in the course of which menacing threats or coercive infliction of physical pain were employed.' . . . A 3×3 table yielding a Chi square significant at the .05 level suggests that episodes of lesser offensiveness are concentrated in the fall and more offensive episodes in the spring." Barrington adds, "The professional journals are full of similar articles where careful methodology is used on trivial problems."[4]

Social scientists, not surprisingly, are much less sanguine about their calling than natural scientists are about theirs. In 1959, Bernard Berelson asked some 2,300 young scholars and scientists, "How would you characterize the current state of health of your discipline—its intellectual vigor, development, progress, etc.?" The percentage of people in various fields who gave "very satisfactory" as their answer was as follows:[5]

Mathematics and Statistics	61
Physics	58
Biology	46
Chemistry	42
Botany	38
Zoology	33
Geology	30
Psychology	28
Economics	21
Political Science	13
Sociology	13

Because the government is spending so much more money for social research, social scientists may be somewhat happier with their situation than they were in 1959. But it is clear that they are much less sure that they are on the right track than natural scientists are. In 1964, for instance, Robert MacLeod of Cornell, who was then president of the American Psychological Association, gloomily asked his fellow psychologists, "Would our students not be equally well, or perhaps even better, educated if the time now devoted to psychology were invested in other subjects?" Noting that psychology has been defined as "what psychologists do in their laboratories," MacLeod went on to say, "For a growing proportion of psychologists the laboratory is remembered as a rather dismal place where meaningless but still sacred puberty rites were conducted, after completion of which they were judged ready to venture forth into the real world, usually to battle against the medical profession for a place in the upper income brackets. . . . Is psychology a subject, or a profession, or a profession disguised as a subject, or just a name in search of a meaning?"[6] One does not hear this sort of thing from leading physicists or astronomers or biologists. Compared with MacLeod's jeremiad, even Paul Weiss's remarks about biological research, which are quoted in Chapter X, have an almost complacent ring.

It can be argued that the social and the natural sciences differ mainly in that the former are at an earlier stage of evolution. Certainly economics is much "harder" and more mathematical than it was thirty years ago, and is having a much greater impact on the conduct of practical affairs. But in view of differences such as those I have listed, it seemed sensible to me to think of American social scientists as a distinct species, and to leave it to someone else to describe their habits and ecology.

Notes

I / On Becoming a Scientist

1. National Science Foundation, *Reviews of Data on Science Resources*, No. 11 (December, 1966), pp. 1, 8. The 1966 National Register lists 243,000 scientists, 186,000 of whom are in the natural sciences. The National Science Foundation estimates that the Register includes about two-thirds of all scientists eligible for listing, and I arrived at the figure of "nearly 300,000" by crude extrapolation. My estimate that about a third of the natural scientists have Ph.D.'s was arrived at the same way.

2. W. Lloyd Warner and James C. Abegglen, *Big Business Leaders in America* (New York, Harper and Brothers, 1955), p. 15; Anselm L. Strauss and Lee Rainwater, *The Professional Scientist: A Study of American Chemists* (Chicago, Aldine Publishing Co., 1962), p. 232; and Bernard Berelson, *Graduate Education in the United States* (New York, McGraw-Hill, 1960), p. 154.

3. "The Scientists," *Fortune*, 38 (October, 1948), pp. 106–112, and 166–176.

4. R. H. Knapp and H. B. Goodrich, *Origins of American Scientists* (Chicago, University of Chicago Press, 1952), pp. 278–284, and 325–327.

5. The shift that took place after World War Two is shown by an analysis of the undergraduate training of men and women who earned Ph.D.'s, or who won competitive prizes or fellowships at the graduate level, between 1946 and 1951. In the sci-

ences, the institutions that had graduated the largest number of such people in proportion to their enrollment included many of the same colleges that had ranked highest in the earlier study by Knapp and Goodrich. But the twenty institutions that had been most productive in terms of scientists-per-thousand-graduates now included eight universities, among them Harvard, Princeton, and Cornell. (Robert H. Knapp and Joseph J. Greenbaum, *The Younger American Scholar: His Collegiate Origins* [Chicago, University of Chicago Press, 1953], pp. 103–107.)

6. National Science Foundation, *Fourteenth Annual Report for the Fiscal Year Ended June 30, 1964*, p. 38.

7. In 1958, several thousand graduate students answered questions about their family backgrounds, and 56 percent of the scientists in the sample said that their fathers were unskilled or skilled workers or tradesmen, or had supervisory jobs at the lowest management level. (James A. Davis, *Stipends and Spouses: The Finances of American Arts and Science Graduate Students* [Chicago, The University of Chicago Press, 1962], pp. 25, 162.)

8. For example, the Class of 1965 at Harvard included sixty-seven graduates of the six fashionable schools—St. Mark's, St. Paul's, Groton, Milton, Middlesex, and St. George's—sometimes referred to collectively as St. Grottlesex. Only two of the sixty-seven, or 3 percent, were planning to begin immediately on graduate work in one of the natural sciences. By contrast, 15 percent of their Harvard classmates who were graduates of public high schools had such plans. I am grateful to Mr. Richard G. King, former director of Harvard's Office for Graduate and Career Plans, for furnishing me with these figures.

9. Seymour Warkov, *Subsidies for Graduate Students* (Chicago, National Opinion Research Center/University of Chicago, 1964), pp. 55, 59–60.

10. It has been estimated that in 1960–61 there were about 28,000 full-time graduate students in the natural sciences at American universities, and that 18,000 of these, or 64 percent, had federal fellowships or training grants, or were working as research assistants on federally supported projects. (Harold Orans, *The Effects of Federal Programs on Higher Education*

[Washington, D.C., The Brookings Institution, 1962], p. 70.) As far back as 1917, however, most graduate students were getting stipends of one sort or another. In that year, a speaker at the annual meeting of the Association of American Universities reported that he had sent questionnaires to all of the 630 persons who had earned Ph.D.'s in the United States in the preceding year. Of the 530 who responded, he said, all but 49 had held scholarships, fellowships, or assistantships while at graduate school. (Berelson, *fn.*, p. 148.) My authority for the statement about fellowships in physics in the 1930's is Samuel Goudsmit, editor of *Physical Review Letters*, as quoted by Daniel Lang in *From Hiroshima to the Moon* (New York, Simon and Schuster, 1959), p. 218.

11. This is purely a guess, based on personal observation and some rough calculations of the frequency with which Jewish names appear among the contributors to scientific journals. Anne Roe, in *The Making of a Scientist* (New York, Dodd Mead, 1952), notes that five of the sixty-four eminent scientists who were the subject of her study came from Jewish homes. The *Fortune* survey is reported in Francis Bello, "The Young Scientists," *Fortune*, XLIX (June, 1954), p. 143.

12. In 1946, the City Council of Greater New York unanimously adopted an 81-page report in which the five medical schools of the New York area were found guilty of discrimination. At Columbia's College of Physicians and Surgeons, and at Cornell Medical College, the percentage of Jewish students had dropped from 14 percent in 1920 to less than 5 percent in 1940. (Alfred L. Shapiro, "Racial Discrimination in Medicine," *Jewish Social Studies*, April, 1948.) The statement that there was little discrimination against Jewish students in graduate schools of arts and sciences is hard to prove, but the files of the American Jewish Committee, and my own interviews, yield no significant evidence to the contrary. Discrimination against Jews in academic life in the late 1920's is discussed in Heywood Broun and George Britt, *Christians Only* (New York, Vanguard Press, 1931), pp. 120, 183.

13. Theodore Caplow and Reece J. McGee, *The Academic Marketplace* (Garden City, New York, Anchor Books/Double-

day, 1965), p. 194 (originally published in 1958). In 1962, the American Jewish Committee noted that although fewer than ½ of 1 percent of the executives of major American corporations were Jewish, there had been "a sharp improvement . . . in hiring and promotion for technical areas and in research jobs," and that discrimination in this area was "no longer a problem." The quotations are from an unpublished report, "Employment Discrimination Against Jews in Major Industries."

14. Caplow and McGee, pp. 95, 194.

15. In making up this list, I relied mainly on a study begun in 1964 by the American Council on Education, the results of which have been published in Allan M. Cartter, *An Assessment of Quality in Graduate Education: A Comparative Study of Graduate Departments in 29 Academic Disciplines* (Washington, D.C., American Council on Education, 1966). At the request of Dr. Cartter, approximately 4,000 scientists and scholars, all of whom were teaching at universities, rated graduate faculties in their respective fields as Distinguished; Strong; Good; Adequate; Marginal; or Not Sufficient To Provide Adequate Doctoral Training. The twelve institutions I have named are among the thirteen that Cartter has listed as "leading" on the strength of their having the highest average scores, and at least two departments in the "Distinguished" category (P. 107). The thirteenth was Rockefeller University (formerly the Rockefeller Institute), which I left off my list because it offers doctorates only in the biological sciences. Other universities with at least one "Distinguished" department in the natural sciences were Pennsylvania (pharmacology), Johns Hopkins (zoology), N.Y.U. (mathematics), and Cornell (physics).

16. The figures in this paragraph—but not the judgments about faculty quality—are taken from *Doctorate Recipients From United States Universities, 1958–1966* (Washington, D.C., Publication 1489 of the National Academy of Sciences, 1967), pp. 124–138.

17. *The Federal Government and Education*, Committee on Education and Labor, U.S. House of Representatives, 88th Congress, 1st session, 1963; House Document No. 159, p. 20.

18. Berelson, *fn.*, p. 105.

19. Meg Greenfield, "Science Goes to Washington," *The Reporter* (September 26, 1963), p. 23, and Caplow and McGee, p. 193. To see if there had been any significant change since 1958, when *The Academic Marketplace* was published, I checked the educational backgrounds of one hundred scientists, picked at random from the eleventh edition of *American Men of Science* (New York and London, R. R. Bowker Co., 1966), who were promoted during the late 1950's or early 1960's to tenured faculty positions at American colleges and universities. I found only two exceptions to the rule I have stated. One was an associate professor of zoology at Michigan whose degree was from Ohio State, and the other was an associate professor of physics at Berkeley whose degree was from Minnesota.

20. Berelson, *fn.*, p. 178.

21. *Ibid.*, p. 176.

22. The relative quality of scientific work in Europe and America is discussed in Chapter IV, "The Price of Affluence," pp. 129–133.

23. Berelson, p. 153.

24. *Ibid.*, pp. 153, 297.

25. *Proceedings of a Conference on Academic and Industrial Basic Research* (Washington, D.C., National Science Foundation, 1961), p. 70.

26. Published in Cambridge, Mass., by the Belknap Press of Harvard University Press, in 1959. The quotation is from page 29.

27. William G. Bowen, *The Federal Government and Princeton University* (Princeton, N.J., Princeton University, Jan. 1962), pp. 209, 211.

28. Berelson, p. 192.

29. *Ibid.*, p. 194.

30. Nearly two-thirds of the graduate faculty members in the physical and biological sciences who were questioned by Berelson in 1959 agreed that in their fields postdoctoral training was "becoming necessary or highly desirable for proper advancement." (Berelson, p. 191.)

31. *Chemistry: Opportunities and Needs*, A Report on Basic Research in U.S. Chemistry by the Committee for the Survey

of Chemistry (Washington, D.C., Publication No. 1292 of the National Academy of Sciences/National Research Council, 1965), p. 147.

II / *Science for the Sake of Science*

1. *Federal Research and Development Programs*, Hearings before the Select Committee on Government Research, U.S. House of Representatives, 88th Congress, 1st and 2nd sessions, Part 2, (Dec. 11 and 12, 1963, and Jan. 22, 1964), p. 941.
2. Prologue to Max Planck, *Where Is Science Going?* (New York, W. W. Norton & Co., Inc.), p. 7.

III / *The Good Professorial Life*

1. J. D. Bernal, *Science in History*, Third Edition (New York, Hawthorn Books, 1965), p. 362.
2. Everett Mendelsohn, "The Emergence of Science as a Profession in Nineteenth-Century Europe," in *The Management of Scientists*, ed. by Karl Hill (Boston, Beacon Press, 1964), p. 11.
3. *Ibid.*, pp. 15–16.
4. Frederick Rudolph, *The American College and University* (New York, Alfred A. Knopf, 1962), p. 232; Henry Rowland, "The Highest Aim of the Physicist," *American Journal of Science*, VIII (1899), pp. 401–11.
5. James Morgan Hart, *German Universities: A Narrative of Personal Experience* (New York, 1878); quoted in Richard Hofstadter and Walter P. Metzger, *The Development of Academic Freedom in the United States* (New York, Columbia University Press, 1955), p. 376.
6. W. H. Cowley, "Three Curricular Conflicts," *Liberal Education*, 46 (December, 1960), p. 473; quoted in Orlans, p. 55.
7. Of 2,800 graduate students questioned by the National Opinion Research Center in 1958, nearly half of whom were studying one of the natural sciences, seven out of ten said they

would prefer an academic job to anything else. "More students prefer academic jobs than expect them," the NORC reported, "and our follow-up materials suggest that more students expect than get them." Davis, *Stipends and Spouses*, p. 20.

8. Ralph M. Hower and Charles D. Orth, *Managers and Scientists: Some Human Problems in Industrial Research Organizations* (Boston, Harvard University Graduate School of Business Administration, 1963), pp. 136–7.

9. Berelson (p. 83) reports that he analyzed the authorship of articles published in a number of leading scientific journals in 1958. Academic scientists (apparently defined so as to include all scientists not working for the government or in industry) were responsible for 68 percent of the papers in chemistry, 64 percent in physics, and 79 percent in biology. A more recent survey of basic-research papers published in chemical journals indicates that 59 percent are written by academic scientists. (John E. Willard, "Maintaining Leadership in Basic Research," in *Basic Research and National Goals: A Report to the Committee on Science and Astronautics, U.S. House of Representatives, by the National Academy of Sciences* [Washington, D.C., 1965], p. 295.) According to a count I made in 1966, academic scientists are also responsible (as sole or senior authors) for two-thirds of all research reports published in *Science*, the weekly journal of the American Association for the Advancement of Science.

10. Quoted by Warren O. Hagstrom in *The Scientific Community* (New York, Basic Books, 1965), p. 31.

11. Charles Richet, *The Natural History of a Savant* (London and Toronto, J. M. Dent & Sons, 1927), pp. 9, 150. This is a translation by Sir Oliver Lodge of the original French edition, published in Paris in 1923.

12. Yandell Henderson and Maurice R. Davies, *Incomes and Living Costs of a University Faculty* (New Haven, Yale University Press, 1928). The quotation is from p. 11.

13. Between 1949–50 and 1964–65, the average salary of faculty members (all ranks) at thirty-six colleges and universities surveyed biennially by the American Association of University Professors rose from $5,310 to $11,210. The average salary

of a full professor rose from $7,490 to $15,230. (*AAUP Bulletin*, Summer, 1965, p. 249, Table 1, "Trends in Academic Salaries.") The figures for 1966–67 salaries are from *AAUP Bulletin*, Summer, 1967, pp. 142–43, 148, 152.

14. The quotation is from *Responses from the Academic and Other Interested Communities to an Inquiry by the Research and Technical Programs Subcommittee of the Committee on Government Operations*, "Conflicts Between the Federal Research Programs and the Nation's Goals for Higher Education" (part 1), U.S. House of Representatives, 89th Congress, 1st session, June, 1965, p. 23. Surveys at two unidentified private universities, one made in 1959–60 and the other in 1960–61, showed that at both institutions the salaries of full professors averaged about 6 percent higher in the natural sciences than in the humanities. (Orlans, p. 306.)

15. "Supplementation due to salary payments by the federal government . . . is probably sanctioned in most, if not all, departments of engineering and clinical medicine and, outside of such professional departments occurs occasionally at more universities than is generally realized, but usually then affects few persons." (Orlans, p. 124.) However, 67 percent of the scientists at a leading university surveyed in 1960 were drawing summer salaries equivalent to two-ninths of their regular academic pay, the maximum permitted by the university's rule. The survey covered all academic ranks; the percentage of full professors who were on summer salary was no doubt much higher. (*Ibid.*, pp. 128, 307.)

16. Herbert E. Longenecker, *University Faculty Compensation Policies and Practices in the United States* (published for the Association of American Universities by the University of Illinois Press, Urbana, Ill., 1956), p. 73.

17. Daniel S. Greenberg, "Consulting: Advice for a Price Has Become an Important Factor in Finances of Many Scientists," *Science*, 145 (September 25, 1964), pp. 1416–17.

18. These figures are from an unpublished study usually referred to as the Colfax Study.

19. These figures are based on a survey of faculty compensation at forty-one leading liberal arts colleges and major univer-

sities that is made biennially by the AAUP. (*AAUP Bulletin*, Summer, 1967, p. 152.)

20. Erwin O. Smigel, *The Wall Street Lawyer* (New York, The Free Press of Glencoe, 1964), p. 229. About one out of nine orthopedic surgeons recently surveyed by *Medical Economics* magazine had a net income before taxes of $70,000 or more. In radiology, the second most highly paid medical specialty, more than 29 percent of the practitioners were making $50,000 a year or more. (William N. Jeffers, "How the Specialties Compare Financially," *Medical Economics*, 44, No. 3 [Feb. 6, 1967], pp. 74–76.)

21. Analysis of a sample of 500 men and women with Ph.D.'s in the natural sciences, picked at random from the 11th Edition of *American Men of Science*, indicates that: (a) two out of five scientists with Ph.D.'s teach at American colleges or universities; and (b) more than half of them teach at institutions that were given either an "A" or a "B" rating in the AAUP's 1965–66 salary survey. Average compensation (nine-month salary plus fringe benefits) of full professors at each of the 120 colleges and universities in the "B" category was at least $14,960; at the twenty-eight institutions in the "A" category the average was at least $18,720. (*AAUP Bulletin*, Summer, 1966, p. 151.) In 1966–67, the average compensation of a full professor rose by about $1,000. (*Ibid.*, Summer, 1967, p. 137, Table 1.)

22. Bentley Glass, "The Academic Scientist, 1940–1960," *Science*, 132 (September 2, 1960), p. 600.

23. Seymour Tilson, "Educating the Scientist," *International Science and Technology*, March, 1965, pp. 47–48.

24. Orlans, pp. 4, 98.

25. Anne Roe, "The Psychology of Scientists," in *The Management of Scientists*, p. 60; Roe, "Changes in Scientific Activities with Age," *Science*, 150 (October 15, 1965), p. 316; Orlans, p. 94.

26. Raymond M. Hughes, "Research in American Universities and Colleges," in *Research—A National Resource* (National Resources Committee, 1938), Vol. 1, p. 179, quoted by Orlans, pp. 56–7; Orlans, p. 94.

27. J. B. Adams, "Megaloscience," *Science*, 148 (June 18, 1965), p. 1562.

28. Jacques Barzun, *The House of Intellect* (New York, Harper & Brothers, 1959), p. 188.

29. Derek J. de Solla Price, *Little Science, Big Science* (New York, Columbia University Press, 1963), pp. 84–85.

30. Daniel S. Greenberg, "Summer: The 'Climate' is Changed for University Scientists and the Federal Government Did It," *Science*, 148 (May 7, 1965), p. 776; Dael Wolfle, "Gordon Research Conferences," *Science*, 148 (April 30, 1965), p. 583.

31. *Responses from the Academic and Other Interested Communities* (part 2), p. 415. Dr. Selove pointed out that in 1964 the National Science Foundation, which spreads its money around more widely than most of the government agencies that subsidize basic research at educational institutions, was supporting only twelve research projects in physics that were being carried out at liberal arts colleges. (*Conflicts Between the Federal Research Programs and the Nation's Goals for Higher Education*, Hearings before a subcommittee of the Committee on Government Operations, 89th Congress, 1st sess., June 14, 1965, p. 15.) In 1965, more than half of all United States colleges and universities (not counting junior colleges) got no support from the government for research of any kind. (*Federal Support for Academic Science and Other Educational Activities in Universities and Colleges, Fiscal Year 1965* [NSF 66–30], prepared by the National Science Foundation for the Office of Science and Technology, pp. 48–49.)

32. Ninety-one percent of all students who held National Science Foundation fellowships on entering graduate school in the years 1954–59 had done their undergraduate work at universities. (Berelson, p. 132.)

33. Gerald Holton, "Scientific Research and Scholarship: Notes toward the Design of Proper Scales," *Daedalus*, Spring, 1962, p. 371.

34. Cartter, p. 62. The assessment was based on the opinions of approximately four thousand scholars and scientists at 106 universities who filled out questionnaires in 1964 and who were asked, among other things, how their time was divided during

the academic year. Senior members of chemistry departments said they spent 52 percent of their time on instruction, 19 percent on administration, 19 percent on research and writing, and 9 percent on other professional activities, such as consulting, speaking, and attending conferences. Senior members of physics departments said they spent 48 percent of their time on instruction, 20 percent on administration, 23 percent on research and writing, and 10 percent on other activities (p. 68).

35. Bernice T. Eiduson, *Scientists: Their Psychological World*, (New York, Basic Books, 1962), p. 160.

36. Orlans, p. 50.

37. J. Robert Oppenheimer, "The Relations of Research to the Liberal University," in Edgar N. Johnson and others, *Freedom and the University* (Ithaca, New York, Cornell University Press, 1950), pp. 100–101.

38. Richard Wolfgang, "Pure Research, Cultism, and the Undergraduate," *Science*, 150 (Dec. 17, 1965), p. 1564.

39. Logan Wilson, *The Academic Man* (New York, Octagon Books, 1964), p. 188. (Originally published in 1942.)

40. *Responses from the Academic and Other Interested Communities* (Part 2) p. 256.

41. Anne Roe, "Changes in Scientific Activities with Age," *Science*, pp. 317–18.

42. Christopher Jencks, "A New Breed of B.A.'s: Some Alternatives to Unrest," *New Republic*, 153 (October 23, 1965), pp. 18–19.

43. Cartter, p. 68. Senior members of physics departments were shown to be spending 19 percent of their time on undergraduate teaching and 20 percent on administration. In chemistry, the figures were 23 and 19 percent (p. 62).

44. Floyd Reeves and others, *The University Faculty* (The University of Chicago Survey, Vol. III, Chicago, University of Chicago Press, 1933), p. 163; Orlans, p. 321; Cartter, pp. 22, 68.

45. Caplow & McGee, pp. 97–8.

46. Quoted by Diana M. Crane in "The Environment of Discovery" (Doctoral dissertation, Columbia University, 1964), p. 154.

47. Anne Roe, "Changes in Scientific Activities with Age," *Science*, p. 318.

48. Eiduson, *Scientists: Their Psychological World*, p. 189.

49. Anne Roe, "The Psychology of Scientists," in *The Management of Scientists*, p. 60.

50. Wayne Dennis, "Age and Productivity Among Scientists," *Science*, 123 (April 27, 1956), p. 724.

51. Anne Roe, "Changes in Scientific Activities with Age," *Science*, p. 317.

52. I. I. Rabi, "Science in the Satisfaction of Human Aspiration," in *The Scientific Endeavor: Centennial Celebration of the National Academy of Sciences* (New York, The Rockefeller Institute Press, 1965), p. 309.

IV / *The Price of Affluence*

1. Merle A. Tuve, "Basic Research in Private Research Institutes," in *Symposium on Basic Research*, ed. by Dael Wolfle (Washington, D.C., Publication No. 56 of the American Association for the Advancement of Science, 1959), p. 171.

2. Victor K. McElheny, "France Considers Significance of Nobel Awards," *Science*, 150 (November 19, 1965), pp. 1013–1015.

3. Don K. Price, "The Scientific Establishment," in *Scientists and National Policy-Making*, ed. by Robert Gilpin and Christopher Wright (New York and London, Columbia University Press, 1964), p. 39; reprinted from American Philosophical Society, *Proceedings*, 106, No. 3 (June, 1962).

4. *Responses from the Academic and Other Interested Communities* (pt. 2), p. 415.

5. *Proceedings of the University of California Thirteenth All-University Faculty Conference*, University of California, April 1958, p. 50; quoted in Orlans, pp. 200–201.

6. *Responses from the Academic and Other Interested Communities* (pt. 2), p. 500.

7. Orlans, pp. 201–203. Some administrators make no bones about this. Gerard Piel, publisher of *Scientific American*, has

cited the case of "one university president, celebrating a substantial benefaction from the Atomic Energy Commission, [who] declared to his regents: 'The key to success is the faculty member who can and does attract grants, contracts and other financial assistance.' " ("The Treason of the Clerks," *Proceedings of the American Philosophical Society*, 109 [October, 1965], p. 264.)

8. Lawrence S. Kubie, "Some Unsolved Problems of the Scientific Career," *American Scientist*, 42 (1954), p. 111.

9. Participants in the conference on basic research, held at Princeton in 1960, to which I referred in Chapter I, deplored the fact that so many young scientists feel this way. The summary of their discussion on this point reads, in part: "The present atmosphere of intense competition for jobs, for prestige, and for research grants places too much emphasis on the achievement of quick and fairly certain results at the expense of the slower and more valuable maturing of the scientist. The younger men have become concerned with making their reputation as quickly as possible; to do this they are forced to choose problems they are sure will yield publishable results in a short time, rather than the more difficult problems with uncertain results. Some of the participants in this Conference felt that the research of younger men is becoming more superficial and even trivial, although in the past it was the younger men who made the deepest and most stirring contributions to science." (*Proceedings of a Conference on Academic and Industrial Basic Research*, p. 75.) Nothing was said in the summary about the possibility that more young scientists might pick significant problems if older scientists would reward those who did so with grants and jobs.

10. Robert K. Merton, "Priorities in Scientific Discovery: A Chapter in the Sociology of Science," *American Sociological Review*, 22 (December, 1957), p. 636.

11. Eiduson, *Scientists: Their Psychological World*, p. 180.

12. Quoted in Theodore Berland, *The Scientific Life* (New York, Coward-McCann, 1962), p. 131.

13. Hagstrom, *The Scientific Community*, p. 142.

14. Warren Weaver, "A Great Age for Science," in *Goals for Americans, The Report of the President's Commission on National Goals* (New York, Prentice-Hall, 1960), p. 115.

15. *Biomedical Science and Its Administration: A Study of the National Institutes of Health* (Washington, D.C., the White House, 1965), p. 22.

16. Orlans, p. 253.

17. *Federal Support for Academic Science and Other Educational Activities in Universities and Colleges, Fiscal Year 1965*, pp. 21, 25. Most of the money these institutions received was for research and development, but the totals given in this report also include institutional grants and graduate fellowships.

18. Edwin R. Embree, "In Order of Their Eminence," *Atlantic Monthly*, 155 (June, 1945), pp. 652–64.

19. Orlans, p. 260.

20. A study in 1964 by the Committee for the Survey of Chemistry of the National Academy of Sciences indicated that junior faculty members at universities with small graduate chemistry departments were getting an average of less than $2,000 a year from university research funds. At universities with larger (and in most cases more prestigious) departments, young chemists a year out of graduate school were getting an average of more than $7,000 each. (*Chemistry:Opportunities and Needs*, p. 156.)

21. Bowen, *The Federal Government and Princeton University*, p. 9.

22. *Responses from the Academic and Other Interested Communities* (pt. 2), pp. 181–82.

23. Letter from Vernon W. Lippard, *Science*, 155 (March 24, 1967), pp. 1490–92.

24. Quoted in D. S. Greenberg, "Money for Research: LBJ's Advisers Urge Scientists to Seek Public Support," *Science*, 156 (May 19, 1967), pp. 921–922.

25. Joseph H. Simons, "Scientific Research in the University," *American Scientist*, 48 (March, 1960), p. 86.

26. Bernice T. Eiduson, "Scientists as Advisors and Consultants in Washington," *Bulletin of the Atomic Scientists*, XXII, No. 8 (October, 1966), p. 27.

27. *Responses from the Academic and Other Interested Communities* (part 2), p. 394; *Ibid.* (part 1), pp. 36–7.

28. Daniel S. Greenberg, "When Pure Science Meets Pure Politics," *The Reporter*, 30 (March 12, 1964), pp. 39–41.

29. Tuve, pp. 183–84.

30. "Career Awards: No More New Ones Will Be Made Under NIH Program," *Science*, 146 (Dec. 25, 1964), p. 1662. See also letter from Irwin D. J. Bross of the Roswell Park Memorial Institute, Buffalo, in *Science*, 147 (March 19, 1965), p. 1395.

31. *International Science and Technology*, Sept., 1965, p. 60.

32. *Federal Support of Basic Research in Institutions of Higher Learning*, a report by the Committee on Science and Public Policy of the National Academy of Sciences (Washington, D.C., National Academy of Sciences/National Research Council, 1964), p. 83.

33. *Responses from the Academic and Other Interested Communities* (pt. 2), p. 440.

34. "American Newsletter," *New Scientist*, 349 (July 25, 1963), p. 185.

35. *Physics: Survey and Outlook, A Report on the Present State of U.S. Physics and its Requirements for Future Growth*, by the Physics Survey Committee, National Academy of Sciences/National Research Council (Washington, D.C., National Academy of Sciences/National Research Council, 1966), pp. 19–21; Saunders MacLane, "Leadership and Quality in Science," in *Basic Research and National Goals*, pp. 192–194; *Chemistry: Opportunities and Needs*, pp. 30–32. An analysis of chemical journals published in 1960 in West Germany, Japan, the Soviet Union, and the British Commonwealth nations showed that nearly half of all references to research carried out in other countries—i.e., other than the country in which a particular journal was published—were references to research done in the United States. Although scientists in each country tend to refer most often to research done by their compatriots, in the British Commonwealth journals that were surveyed there were more references to work done in the United States than to the work of British Commonwealth chemists.

36. "With Hitler's help, the U.S. had taken over world leadership in physics," Francis Bello noted in *Fortune* in 1960. "Working in the U.S. in 1945, along with Einstein, Fermi, and Segrè, were such gifted foreigners . . . as Otto Stern and James

Franck (both Nobel Laureates), Felix Bloch (to share the Nobel Prize in 1952 with Edward Purcell for his work on nuclear resonance), John von Neumann (the mathematical genius who died in 1957), Edward Teller (key contributor to the H-bomb), George E. Uhlenbeck and Samuel A. Goudsmit (inventors of the fruitful concept of electron spin in quantum theory), Maria G. Mayer (who was to devise the important shell model of the atomic nucleus), George Gamow (the ingenious student of cosmology), Bruno Rossi (a top authority on cosmic rays), and Victor Weisskopf, Hans Bethe, and Eugene Wigner—all three world leaders in quantum theory." (Francis Bello, "Great American Scientists: The Physicists," *Fortune*, LXI (March, 1960), p. 233.) Ten of the sixteen foreign-born physicists mentioned by Bello came to the United States as refugees. This and succeeding articles in *Fortune* (Lawrence Lessing, "Great American Scientists: The Chemists," April, 1960; George A. W. Boehm, "Great American Scientists: The Astronomers," May, 1960; and Francis Bello, "Great American Scientists: The Biologists," June, 1960) named forty physicists, chemists, astronomers, and biologists as the most distinguished American scientists in their respective fields. Seven of the forty were refugees.

37. "Russian and U.S. Science: Another View of the 'Gap' " *Science*, 151 (Jan. 28, 1966), p. 432.

38. R. P. Grant, C. P. Huttrer, C. G. Metzner, "Biomedical Science in Europe," *Science*, 146 (Oct. 23, 1964), pp. 493–501.

39. "America, America!" *Réalités* (English language edition), October, 1964, pp. 55–57.

V / *The Styles of Big Science*

1. Warren O. Hagstrom, "Traditional and Modern Forms of Scientific Teamwork," *Administrative Science Quarterly*, IX, No. 3 (December, 1964), p. 251.

2. Melvin Schwartz, "The Conflict Between Productivity and Creativity in Modern Day Physics," *American Behavioral Scientist*, December, 1962, p. 35.

3. Quoted by Harriet A. Zuckerman in "Nobel Laureates in

the United States: A Sociological Study of Scientific Collaboration" (Doctoral dissertation, Columbia University, 1965), p. 238.

4. Schwartz, p. 35.

5. Interview, *International Journal of Science and Technology*, August, 1962, p. 72.

6. L. Kowarski, "Team Work and Individual Work in Research," *CERN Courier*, II (May, 1962), p. 7.

7. Hagstrom, *Administrative Science Quarterly*, p. 254.

8. Quoted by permission of the author.

9. Alvin M. Weinberg, "Impact of Large-Scale Science on the United States," *Science*, 134 (July 21, 1961), p. 161.

10. This quotation is from the text of a talk, "The Coming Age of Biomedical Science," prepared by Alvin M. Weinberg for presentation to the Second NIH International Symposium on "National Policies for Biomedical Research: Structures and Processes for Policy Development," Williamsburg, March 1, 1965.

11. Walter Rosenblith, "On Some Social Consequences of Scientific and Technological Change," *Daedalus*, Summer, 1961, p. 511.

12. *Federal Research and Development Programs*, Hearings before the Select Committee on Government Research, U.S. House of Representatives, 88th Congress, 1st session, Part 1 (Nov. 18, 19, 20, 21, and 22, 1963), p. 612.

13. Zuckerman, p. 75; the percentages of papers by four or more authors have been calculated from figures compiled by Dr. Zuckerman, which she was kind enough to let me use.

14. Hagstrom, *The Scientific Community*, p. 128. The survey cited by Hagstrom was made by Robert Wenkert and Roderic Frederickson, and its main purpose was to determine the use of, and potential demand for, computer services at the university. Their sample included about half of the physical and biological scientists at the university. Some of the results of the survey were reported in *Use of a University Computer Center* (Berkeley: University of California Survey Research Center, 1962).

15. *Physics: Survey and Outlook, A Report on the Present State of U.S. Physics and its Requirements for Future Growth*, p. 97.

16. *Biomedical Science and Its Administration*, pp. 40–41.

17. John Walsh, "NIH: Demand Increases for Applications of Research," *Science*, 153 (July 8, 1966), p. 150.
18. *Biomedical Science and its Administration*, p. 42.

VI / Scientists Without Students

1. Crane, "The Environment of Discovery," p. 161.
2. *Studies of Macromolecular Biosynthesis*, ed, by Richard B. Roberts, Carnegie Institution of Washington, Publication No. 624 (Washington, D.C., 1964), p. 687.
3. "Annual Report of the Director of the Department of Terrestrial Magnetism," in *Carnegie Institution of Washington Year Book 63* (Washington, D.C., Carnegie Institution, 1964), p. 295.
4. Alvin M. Weinberg, "Science, Choice, and Human Values," *Bulletin of the Atomic Scientists*, 22 (April, 1966), pp. 9–10.
5. Weinberg, "The Coming Age of Biomedical Science."

VII / The Vineyards of Utility

1. U.S. National Resources Planning Board, II. *Industrial Research*, Sec. IV, p. 176; cited by Bernard Barber in *Science and the Social Order*, revised edition (New York, Collier Books, 1962), p. 215.
2. "Stock Sprees," *Wall Street Journal*, April 24, 1961, pp. 1, 12. Quoted in Strauss and Rainwater, p. 9.
3. In 1966, the National Register of Scientific and Technical Personnel listed 132,000 scientists who were employed by federal, state, or local government agencies, by nonprofit organizations, or by business or industry. (National Science Foundation, *Reviews of Data on Science Resources*, No. 11, December 1966.) Of the 87,000 scientists listed as working for educational institutions, perhaps 3,000 were employed at research centers like the Los Alamos Scientific Laboratory, or Johns Hopkins' Applied Physics Laboratory, which are managed by universities but which are in effect government laboratories. About one-third of

all scientists eligible for inclusion in the National Register are not listed because they fail to return the questionnaires that are sent to them. After adding 132,000 and 3,000, I therefore multiplied the total by 1.5 to arrive at the figures of "more than 200,-000." The estimates I have given as to how many Ph.D.'s in various fields work for government or industry are based on Lindsey R. Harmon, *Profiles of Ph.D's in the Sciences: Summary Report on Follow-Up of Doctorate Cohorts, 1935–1960* (Washington, D.C., Publication 1293 of the National Academy of Sciences/National Research Council, 1965).

4. National Science Foundation, *Reviews of Data on Science Resources*, No. 9, August, 1966 ("Resources for Scientific Activities at Universities and Colleges, 1964), p. 13, Table B.

5. "The Treason of the Clerks," p. 265.

6. Quoted by Daniel Lang in *An Inquiry into Enoughness* (New York, McGraw-Hill, 1965), p. 105.

7. Lawrence H. O'Neill, "Building Morale in Engineering," *Columbia University Forum*, Summer, 1964, pp. 32, 34.

VIII / *The Industrial Labyrinth*

1. Quoted by Hubert Kay in "Harnessing the R. and D. Monster," *Fortune*, LXXI (January, 1965), p. 160.

2. These figures are derived from the tables in Harmon, *Profiles of Ph.D's in the Sciences*.

3. Bruce F. Gordon and Ian C. Ross, "Professionals and the Corporation," *Research Management*, 5 (1962), p. 498.

4. John Walsh, "Bell Labs: A Systems Approach to Innovation is the Main Thing," *Science*, 153 (July 22, 1966), pp. 393–396. Walsh reports that in early 1966, 530 scientists and engineers were engaged in fundamental research at Bell Laboratories; according to a member of the Laboratories staff whom I consulted, most of them have the sort of autonomy I have described.

5. Richard R. Nelson, "The Link Between Science and Invention: The Case of the Transistor," in *The Rate and Direction of Inventive Activity: Economic and Social Factors*, published by the National Bureau of Economic Research as Special

Conference Series No. 13 (Princeton, Princeton University Press, 1962), p. 578.

6. Quoted by William Kornhauser in *Scientists in Industry: Conflict and Accommodation* (Berkeley and Los Angeles, University of California Press, 1962), p. 69.

7. Quoted by Charles D. Orth, Joseph C. Bailey, and Francis W. Wolek in *Administering Research and Development: The Behavior of Scientists and Engineers in Organizations* (Homewood, Illinois, Richard D. Irwin & Co., 1964), p. 307.

8. Quoted by Simon Marcson in *The Scientist in American Industry: Some Organizational Determinants in Manpower Utilization* (Princeton, New Jersey, Princeton University Industrial Relations Section, 1960), p. 114.

9. Quoted in Kay, *Fortune*, pp. 163, 196.

10. Lowell W. Steele, "Loyalties," *International Science and Technology*, February, 1963, p. 57.

11. Quoted in Orth, Bailey, and Wolek, p. 321.

12. Hower and Orth, p. 128.

13. "The Dual Hierarchy in Research," *Research Management*, Autumn, 1958; reprinted in Orth, Bailey, and Wolek, pp. 425–432.

14. Quoted in Orth, Bailey, and Wolek, pp. 322–325.

15. Cited in C. Wilson Randle, "Problems of R. & D. Management," *Harvard Business Review*, January-February, 1959, pp. 128–136. The survey was made by Booz, Allen and Hamilton, management consultants.

16. Arnold C. Cooper, "R & D is More Efficient in Small Companies," *Harvard Business Review*, May-June, 1964, pp. 75–83.

17. Running through a list of some 4,000 names picked at random from the 11th edition of *American Men of Science*, I found thirty-three people who had switched from industry to university faculties in 1960–65, as against thirteen who had moved in the opposite direction.

18. Nelson, p. 580.

19. Marcson, pp. 69–70.

20. Quoted in F. R. Bichowski, *Industrial Research* (New York, Chemical Publishing Company, 1942), pp. 56–57.

21. Quoted by Donald A. Schon in "Champions for Radical New Inventions," *Harvard Business Review*, March-April, 1963, p. 85.

22. Quoted in Walsh, *Science*, p. 395.

23. James Brian Quinn and James A. Mueller, "Transferring Research Results to Operations," *Harvard Business Review*, January-February, 1963, p. 55.

24. Chris Argyris, "Interpersonal Competence, Organizational Milieu, and Innovation," *Research Management*, IX (March, 1966), p. 87.

25. Steele, "The Role of the Research Manager," General Electric Co., *Research Laboratory Bulletin*, Spring, 1962, pp. 17–18.

26. Kornhauser, pp. 48–49.

27. Morris I. Stein, "Creativity and the Scientist," in Barber and Hirsch, p. 338.

28. E. M. Kipp, "Introduction of the Newly Graduated Scientist to Industrial Research," *Research Management*, III (Spring, 1960), p. 42.

29. Herbert A. Shepard, "Adaptive Processes for Research and Innovation," in *The Management of Scientists*, pp. 130–131.

30. *The Conflict Between the Scientific Mind and the Management Mind* (Princeton, New Jersey, Opinion Research Corporation, 1959); quoted in Kay, *Fortune*, p. 163.

31. American Institute of Physics, *Physics Manpower 1966: Education and Employment Statistics*, pp. 112, 114.

32. Stein, p. 342.

IX / *Movers and Shakers*

1. Robert C. Wood, "Scientists and Politics: The Rise of an Apolitical Elite," in *Scientists and National Policy-Making*, p. 63.

2. S. K. Allison, "The State of Physics; or the Perils of Being Important," *Bulletin of the Atomic Scientists*, VI, No. 1 (January, 1950), p. 3.

3. Quoted in Ralph Sanders, "The Autumn of Power: The

Scientist in the Political Establishment," *Bulletin of the Atomic Scientists*, XXII, No. 8 (October, 1966), p. 24.

4. Lewis C. Mainzer, "The Scientist as Public Administrator," *Western Political Quarterly*, 16 (December, 1963), p. 818.

5. Bernice T. Eiduson, *Bulletin of the Atomic Scientists*, pp. 26–31.

6. *Ibid.*, p. 30.

7. Anne Roe, "The Psychology of the Scientist," *Science*, 134 (August 18, 1961), p. 458.

8. Eiduson, *Bulletin of the Atomic Scientists*, p. 29; the quotations in the following two paragraphs are from pp. 30 and 31 of the same article.

9. Philip H. Abelson, "The President's Science Advisers," *Minerva*, III (Winter, 1965), p. 154.

10. C. P. Snow, *The Two Cultures and the Scientific Revolution* (New York, Cambridge University Press, 1959), p. 11.

11. C. P. Snow, *Science and Government* (Cambridge, Mass., Harvard University Press, 1961), p. 81.

12. Albert Wohlstetter, "Strategy and the Natural Scientists," in *Scientists and National Policy Making*, ed. by Robert Gilpin and Christopher Wright (New York, Columbia University Press, 1964), pp. 217, 218.

13. *Ibid.*, pp. 220, 221. The quotation from Snow is taken from "The Moral Un-Neutrality of Science," address to the 1960 AAAS meeting, reprinted in *Science*, 133 (January 27, 1961), pp. 255–59.

14. The quotation is from Warner R. Schilling, "Scientists, Foreign Policy, and Politics," in *Scientists and National Policy-Making*, p. 154.

15. Quoted in Douglas Hurd, "A Case for the Diplomats," *Bulletin of the Atomic Scientists*, XVI (February, 1960), p. 52.

16. *Testimony of Scientists on Goals of the Nation's Space Program*, Hearings before the U.S. Senate Committee on Aeronautical and Space Sciences, 88th Congress, 1st session, June 10 and 11, 1963, pp. 51, 53.

17. Amitai Etzioni, "When Scientists Testify," *Bulletin of the Atomic Scientists*, XX (October, 1964), p. 26.

18. *Testimony of Scientists on Goals of the Nation's Space Program*, pp. 73–74.

19. *Ibid.*, p. 3.

20. Greenfield, *The Reporter*, p. 22.

21. Robert Gilpin, *American Scientists and Nuclear Weapons Policy* (Princeton, Princeton University Press, 1962), p. 327.

X / *Eden After Twenty Years*

1. The text of the address was reprinted in *Science*, 136 (May 11, 1962), pp. 468–471.

2. Eiduson, *Bulletin of the Atomic Scientists*, p. 27.

3. Price, *Little Science, Big Science*, pp. 33–54.

4. "Prologue" to Max Planck, *Where Is Science Going?* (New York, W. W. Norton & Co., Inc.), p. 7.

5. Louise Elizabeth Merz, "The Graduate School as a Socializing Agency: A Pilot Study of Sociological Aspects of Graduate Training in the Physical Sciences" (Doctoral dissertation, Cornell University, June, 1961), pp. 34, 37, 127.

6. *Ibid.*, p. 35.

7. *Science, An Interview by Donald McDonald with Hans Bethe* (Center for the Study of Democratic Institutions, Santa Barbara, Calif., 1962), pp. 20–21.

8. Norbert Wiener, "Intellectual Honesty and the Contemporary Scientist," *American Behavioral Scientist*, VIII, No. 3 (Nov., 1964), p. 16.

9. Quoted in Berelson, p. 28.

10. Eiduson, *Bulletin of the Atomic Scientists*, p. 27.

11. I. I. Rabi, "The Interaction of Science and Technology," in *The Impact of Science on Technology*, ed. by Aaron W. Warner, Dean Morse, and Alfred S. Eichner (New York, Columbia University Press, 1965), p. 20.

12. Quoted in John Walsh, "NIH: Demand Increases For Applications of Research," *Science*, 153 (July 8, 1966), p. 150.

13. Quoted in Elinor Langer, "LBJ at NIH: President Offers Kind Words for Basic Research," *Science*, 157 (July 28, 1967), p. 404.

14. Harvey Brooks, "Applied Research Definitions, Concepts, Themes," in *Applied Science and Technological Progress: A Report to the Committee on Science and Astronautics, U.S. House of Representatives, by the National Academy of Sciences* (Washington, D.C., May 25, 1967), p. 47.

15. *Ibid.*, p. 58.

16. "Excerpts from Ruina Report," *Science*, 153 (July 8, 1966), p. 150.

17. A. B. Sabin, "Collaboration for Accelerating Progress in Medical Research," *Science*, 156 (June 23, 1967), p. 1570.

Appendix / *Why Social Scientists Don't Fit In*

1. Orlans, p. 101.

2. *Ibid.*, p. 98.

3. *The Use of Social Research in Federal Domestic Programs: A Staff Study for the Research and Technical Programs Subcommittee of the Committee on Government Operations*, U.S. House of Representatives, 90th Congress, 1st session; Part IV—Current Issues in the Administration of Federal Social Research, p. 35.

4. Barrington Moore, "Strategy in Social Science," in *Sociology on Trial*, ed. by Maurice Stein and Arthur Vidich (Englewood Cliffs, N.J., Prentice-Hall, Inc., 1963), pp. 77. The article cited by Moore is by C. Kirkpatrick and E. Kanin, and appeared in *American Sociological Review*, XXII, No. 1 (Feb. 1957); the passage Moore quotes is on p. 53.

5. Berelson, pp. 211–212.

6. Robert B. MacLeod, "The Teaching of Psychology and the Psychology We Teach," presidential address read at Division 2, American Psychological Association, Los Angeles, September, 1964; printed in *American Psychologist*, May, 1965. The passages quoted are on pp. 345 and 350.

INDEX

A

A Note About the Author

SPENCER KLAW was born in New York City in 1920. After graduation from Harvard, where he was president of *The Crimson*, he began a newspaper career in San Francisco and Washington. This was soon interrupted for war service in France, for which the author received the Croix de Guerre. After the war, he covered the United Nations for the United Press, spent five years on *The New Yorker*, was an assistant to the Sunday Editor of the New York *Herald Tribune*, and served as an associate editor of *Fortune*. Since 1960, he has free-lanced, writing for *Harper's*, *Playboy*, *The Saturday Evening Post*, *Esquire*, *The Reporter*, and many other magazines. He lives in New York City and Cornwall, Connecticut, with his wife, who is an editor of American Heritage and Horizon. The Klaws have two daughters.